Knowing the B.A.S.I.I.C.S.

7 Common Early Signs of Ovarian Cancer

Trish Kifer

Wishing you,
Strength, Love,
Hope & Courage
Always!

All my best—
Trish Kifer

Foreword by Saketh R. Guntupalli, MD, and Jacqueline Fields, MD

Knowing the B.A.S.I.I.C.S.

Although the author and publisher have made every effort to ensure that the information in this book was correct at press time, the author and publisher do not assume and hereby disclaim any liability to any party for any loss, damage, or disruption caused by errors or omissions, whether such errors or omissions result from negligence, accident, or any other cause.

Adherence to all applicable laws and regulations, including international, federal, state and local governing professional licensing, business practices, advertising, and all other aspects of doing business in the US, Canada or any other jurisdiction is the sole responsibility of the reader and consumer.

Neither the author nor the publisher assumes any responsibility or liability whatsoever on behalf of the consumer or reader of this material. Any perceived slight of any individual or organization is unintentional.

The resources in this book are provided for informational purposes only and should not be used to replace the specialized training and professional judgment of a health care or mental health care professional.

Neither the author nor the publisher can be held responsible for the use of the information provided within this book. Please always consult a trained professional before making any decision regarding treatment of yourself or others.

Ebook - ISBN# 978-1-7379664-0-1

Paperback - ISBN # 978-1-7379664-1-8

www.hope-journeys.com

Editor: Margaret A. Harrell, https://margaretharrell.com

Cover design and formatting by Cutting-edge-studio.com

Disclaimer

I based this book on my personal experience. I am not a doctor. This book does not intend to be a replacement for any medical advice. It supports going to see your doctor regularly, especially if you have symptoms that require a diagnosis or medical attention

The lists of ovarian-cancer symptoms in Chapter 5 are taken from Memorial Sloan Kettering Cancer Center and Gynecologic Oncology at the University of Colorado, for which I give grateful acknowledgment.

trishkifer@hope-journeys.com

Fort Collins, CO

www.hope-journeys.com

Knowing the B.A.S.I.I.C.S.

Can Save Your Life!

7 Common Early Signs of Ovarian Cancer

Bloating, **A**bnormal uterine blood, **S**tomach feels full, **I**ndigestion, **I**ncontinence, **C**onstant pain in abdomen, and **S**ex is painful.

An inspiring ovarian cancer survivor story

Trish Kifer

Foreword by Saketh R. Guntupalli, MD, and Jacqueline Fields, MD

Dedicated to you!

If life circumstances were a deck of cards, and you got dealt a card that rocked your world, would you want to give it back?
Requesting a re-deal, in hopes for a better one!
My card.
Stage 3C ovarian cancer.
I thought for sure it was a misdeal.
Then it occurred to me, if I give it back, what if I get one that is worse?
I was dealt this hand for a reason.
It was a sign from the universe.
A Divine Moment
of
*Healing * Awareness * Purpose*
That moment guided me to write to you!

Go confidently in the direction of your dreams! Live the life you've imagined. As you simplify your life, the laws of the universe will be simpler. **——Henry David Thoreau**

Contents

Contents

Foreword

By Saketh Guntupalli, MD., Fellow of the American College of Surgeons

You, your greatest advocate . . .

Cancer is the great equalizer. Whether you are a famous actress or a waitress completing a fourteen-hour shift, the fear, dread, and uncertainty after someone tells you that you have cancer is the same. It affects the rich and the poor, the famous and the unknown, the king and the pauper. While some cancers are more curable than others, a unique cancer that affects women is ovarian cancer. Ovarian cancer is simply different. The ovaries in many ways define womanhood, and when cancer affects these organs the sense of loss and fear is somehow compounded. I see this in my practice as women express the same emotions that all cancer patients experience, tempered however by a loss that is unique.

Sadly, most women who present with ovarian cancer are already an advanced stage at diagnosis. This is despite the fact that most women complain of symptoms for months, if not years, which go unacknowledged by our society and, sadly, even the health care industry. It saddens me, daily, to see women in my office complain of these symptoms and hear about the nurse, ER doctor, primary care physician and even gynecologist brush off these symptoms as unimpressive. This is the single most significant reason that women are diagnosed at a late stage—a failure of society and medicine to prioritize these issues and symptoms as a potential cancer.

Knowing the B.A.S.I.I.C.S. is a landmark work that is a must read for any woman, particularly those approaching middle age. Trish beautifully relates her story in a thoughtful and provoking manner that relates the basic symptoms—which she herself experienced—which ultimately turned out to be ovarian cancer. This work is vital for woman to know their bodies and, most important, advocate for themselves. No person, spouse, parent, or child will be more of advocate for your health than yourself! Please continue to push physicians, nurses, and family to take symptoms seriously and nurture the idea that you (the patient) know your body. And when you sense that something is wrong—it probably is. The best teachers I have had in a fifteen-year career in women's health have been my patients—those who taught me from a firsthand view the importance of being a health care advocate.

Foreword 2

By Jacqueline Fields, MD

Mindfulness *Advocacy* Healing

I found this book to be an indispensable perspective for people going through cancer and all women in general. The cancer journey is so difficult, but Trish describes beautifully, how you must create a team you trust and ensure you do not operate in fear. Her wisdom teaches one to become mindful and be your own best advocate throughout the journey. I have been a primary care physician for more than twenty-five years and I have been Trish's physician for more than fifteen years.

To see how Trish navigated her diagnosis, treatment, and healing was a true gift to witness. This book is the last step of her healing, which ensures all she learned is sent out for others to have as a gift and a guide. The concepts you will learn in this book are very important. *Knowing the B.A.S.I.I.C.S.* CAN TRULY SAVE YOUR LIFE. This is a MUST read. ENJOY!

Introduction

Are you a reader who likes to flip to the end of the book? In this case, you do not need to do that. Sorry, I spoiled the ending in the subtitle. A cancer survivor story! With many stories, it is not so much about the beginning or ending as the journey in between. Stories are timeless. That is what makes them extraordinary. Going through this whole storytelling, writing process, I am reminded that everyone has a story. When shared, they are inspirational and lifesaving.

I started with the end in mind to create a sense of ease. Hearing cancer stories and wondering throughout the whole book if the protagonist made it is heart wrenching. So many people in my life, I have lost to cancer. And I feel like I go through the same pain even if it is someone else's story. It all just hits too close to home!

I am a survivor, and you can be too. I am writing to help you recognize the early signs of ovarian cancer before it is too late. Ignoring simple signs could cost you your life! It is the pinnacle reason why I knew I had to tell my story!

There is an unspoken connection in the universe. I feel it all the time. A connection that runs so deep it is often hard to explain, but I know it is there. The connection of unity is what inspired me to write my story. That oneness is you! The mere fact that this book found you underscores why I think the universe has brought us together.

Reading a healing story can be life changing. I know because it happened to me. Along with my support team and incredible doctors, stories helped me on my journey. They helped me face challenges. Made my hurdles more real and attainable. Words and experiences encouraged me to learn more about cancer, most importantly how to survive it. Stories helped keep my perspective positive. They are one of reasons I felt it imperative to share mine. A way to pay it forward—to play my part in the world. To be a part of the cycle and make things whole and balanced.

Cancer has been around for a millennium! *Fun fact: Queen Mary of England, also known as Bloody Mary, died from what is thought to have been ovarian cancer in the year 1558.* Yet, there is still no cure! There may never be a cure for every cancer. The research is promising, and healing stories can illustrate how to prevent cancer from even occurring! On the smallest of scales, I want to prevent people, especially you, from getting sick! I know it is a big ask, but it doesn't hurt to put it out there.

One by one, story by story, there can be a shift that reverses the epidemic of disease in the world, with cancer at the top of the list. I urge you to communicate with one another and stop hiding behind fear, like I did. There is likely a fighting chance! It is so imperative to pay attention to our bodies. Our bodies know how to create signs to tell us something is wrong. It is our job to listen, in turn act. It is one thing to be aware, and another entirely when followed by action. In my case, listening was life altering. It is my hope that sharing my story will impact your life, inspiring you to have the courage to pay attention to the signs. Pay attention to know when something is not right, see a doctor, and go get checked!

Royalties

15 % of the book royalties will go to these charities

- COCA- Colorado Ovarian Cancer Alliance - local support group
- SHARE- research and support for ovarian and breast cancers
- Alex's Lemonade Stand- support and awareness for childhood cancers

Chapter 1

Healing

> Healing involves making us whole in all aspects of our life. Healing involves employing techniques to remove "dis-ease" and put us at ease at a mental, physical, and spiritual level. —Sant Rajinder Singh Ji Maharaj

The right question, the right doctors, the right perspective will be an imperative part of the healing process. The word *healing* means different things. It comes in many forms. Take kids, for example. When they get hurt, who do they usually go to? Yes, Mom! They go to Mom, especially when they are young. Sorry, dads, this is just how it is sometimes. You, of course, play a huge part. But more times than none, moms always make everything better. Mothers help with the healing process. A hug and a really cool BAND-AID® usually does the trick. Intuitively, children know what they need, who can help, and how to go about getting that help. Validation of how they feel is just as important as, if not more important than, treating the wound itself. Even now as an adult, sometimes all it takes to feel better is just talking to my mom! It takes the right person to help with the healing process, not only physically but mentally as well!

I know that my cancer, my "wound," would not have healed unless I had the right people in my life! I can say this because I am here, writing to you! Even now, I am still flabbergasted by how the RIGHT people came into my path. They knew exactly what to do and how to do it. I am sure you are asking yourself, "How do I find the right people, the right doctor?" That is a good question and might be the most important one you can ask in the beginning. Having the wrong doc can take you down a rabbit hole of uncertainty and unnecessary pain.

In my case, I was truly blessed with the RIGHT doctors from the very beginning. My first appointment, after a couple months of pain in my abdomen, a visit in September 2019, was with my family doctor, Dr. Jackie Fields. She has been my doctor for over fifteen years. I remember feeling in that moment, when there were no answers, just waves of uncertainty. There is nothing more nerve-wracking than sitting in a doctor's office, holding your husband's hand, waiting for the door to open, and anticipating what the doctor has to say. He came with me for support, as he was nervous as to what she might find. He did not want me to be alone. I even told him before the visit that he did not need to come.

I thought that if he did not come, then there would not be any challenging news to hear. I wanted to know and not know all at the same time. I wanted her to say that everything was fine. Nothing going on.

As I was sitting there next to Roger, I looked around the room. It's not a typical patient room. It has warmth about it. Sunny yellow walls, a fireplace with pictures of her kids on the mantel, and photos of different sites in Italy. It was time to start the exam. She was able to feel something on my ovary.

After the exam I remember sitting there with Roger, holding hands, I felt it.

I felt the energy from Dr. Fields. She closes her eyes, takes a breath, and speaks: "I am going to be mindful in what I say."

I felt safe in her words. She told us we would not know anything until we got the computerized tomography (CT) scan back. In the meantime, to understand that if it is cancer, I have a plan. The one thing she was adamant about was not to stress! Sitting there, not knowing one way or the other, was hard. I put my energy into staying present. Not to think about the *what ifs*, just breathe.

What I did know was Dr. Fields was on my team, and I was going to be okay, no matter what. Within two weeks I was fast tracked, from blood work to CT scan, first oncology visit, laparoscopy, then first round of chemotherapy. Even though it was only two weeks, it seemed like an eternity.

The ball started rolling the moment Dr. Fields felt there was something on my ovary. She scheduled me to get an ultrasound as soon as possible. The results of the ultrasound lead to blood work and a CT scan as soon as possible The blood work needed was a cancer antigen (CA-125). This marker in the blood, if high, reveals a possible ovarian cancer. Normal range: anything under 35. Mine was 734. In two days, it increased to 1235. Not only were my numbers skyrocketing, but my CT scan showed a 13-centimeter x 11-centimeter mass on my left ovary, and a small mass on my right. I was immediately scheduled with an oncologist, Dr. Saketh Guntupalli. Getting on his caseload was nothing short of a miracle!

But I had to wait a week. Throughout the week I went about life normally. We were upfront and honest with the kids from the get-go. They knew about the mass on my ovaries, and that that was the reason for all the doctor's appointment lately. We told the kids they would be hanging out with friends while we went to this next appointment. They were all for that, and it was comforting to know they would be in good hands. As the week wore on, I was trying not to overthink. Trying to live day by day, not worry too much about the looming appointment.

I was out running errands one morning and found myself clothes shopping. This is something I do not do. I saw a dress that cost $8.00. It fit and I liked it! That also does not happen very often.

The day finally arrived. Friday, September 13, 2019. We headed with the kids down toward the appointment. I decided to wear that dress. I thought maybe on some level the luck I had finding this dress would also give me luck with the news I was about to get from Dr. Guntupalli. "What in the world does this have to do with anything?" you ask. *Well,* I thought to myself, *how could someone give bad news to someone who just got such a great deal on a dress? $8.00! On Friday the 13th, at that?*

I know, I know, very weird, impractical, nonrealistic but in some way it helped. I was scared and so hopeful at the same time. It was my way to deal and try not to get ahead of myself.

Out of all the doctors in the world I got "the guy"! He had credentials out the wazoo, but most of all he was personable and reassuring. I say this with all certainty. He was sitting across from us in a sharp bright blue suit, and I in my dress, Roger in his fancy jeans. We were looking pretty good. This was our first rodeo, and he, I am sure, has seen this too many times to count. As we were sitting in Dr. Guntupalli's office he told us that I had a tumor and most likely it was cancer. Roger at this point said, "Is this terminal?" Dr. Guntupalli responded in a way that basically each case is different, and it was too soon to tell. I was kind of surprised at Roger's comment. It was a hard question, and he had the courage to say it out loud. From Roger's "elephant in the room" terminal question to Dr. Guntupalli's response, I went from despair to hope in a matter of moments.

Roger's next response was, "Can we get the tumors out today?" This is where Doc said that he would have to do an exploratory laparoscopic surgery first to see how exactly big the tumors were and what else was going on in there. Dr. Guntupalli, if he could have done the biopsy that day, would have. That not being the case, we asked, "What percentage do you think that it is cancer?" He gave the odds as maybe a 1 percent chance that it was not. *One percent!* Hey, there's still a chance!

I was banking on being in that 1 percent category. A tumor does not need to be cancer, right?!? I also had my genetic history on my side. My grandma had a tumor on her ovary, and it was benign.

So of course, that is what I thought was going to happen to me. We had an appointment the next Monday to have a laparoscopy surgery done to see what was really going on in there. So that was the next step. A small surgery to see what it was.

As we left the office and started walking out of the building, there was a huge fireplace that we just stood in front of. I just needed a minute to wrap my head around all this. Roger was so incredible, giving me space and being so supportive, as I am sure his mind was racing all over the place as well. Somehow, I felt if I just stayed there, looking at the fire and not leaving, the news would not be real. *The second we walk out the doors, that is when it will all hit me.*

When we walked outside and headed to the car, nothing happened. I felt like I was doing pretty good. This news we got was intense. Roger opened my car door and I got in. Sat down, started to put my seatbelt on; that is when the emotions took over. It was like an out of body experience. It was me crying, but it felt like I was witnessing it through someone else's eyes. By the time he got back to the driver's side, I was a mess! He reached over and we hugged! It was in that moment that I came back into my body. I knew without a shadow of a doubt that I indeed had cancer!

When we left the office, I still had this glimpse of hope that this whole thing would be over by Monday. I truly did. I found out I have tumors on my ovaries on a Friday and had a little peek with the laparoscopic surgery on Monday—and then by Tuesday at the very latest be all done with this tumor business!

Well, as things go in life, that is not what happened. The plan was to do the laparoscopic surgery to see how big the tumors really were and what else was going on in there. If a biopsy proved benign, then and only then would they, while still in surgery, go further—take out the tumors and do a full hysterectomy. That was where I was putting all my energy. I remember thinking I had a 1 percent chance of its not being cancer, and if it was cancer, they were going to take it out right then and there.

Monday morning arrived. I was pleased to have the surgery on Monday morning. Dr. Guntupalli would have had the whole weekend to rest and be fresh for the surgery. My parents were coming up from New Mexico, to help with the kids if it turned out to be a full hysterectomy. We did not want them to make the trip just for the laparoscopy. Not that having a laparoscopic surgery was anything to throw sticks at. Surgery is surgery, right? In my mind, having my parents come up reinforced my thoughts that the medical team was going to get the whole enchilada on Monday. I had this plan in my head, and I was putting all my energy into that plan. Everything was set in motion. Everything was good to go. I was going to have the laparoscopic surgery. In the process, they would see the tumor, take it out, and call it a day. Done and done. I was trying to escape the possibility of the realness of it all.

As the anesthesia wore off, I started to wake up. The first person I saw was Roger. I can barely describe how much it meant to me to have him there. I was not awake for more than three seconds, and he was holding my hand. I knew right then that they were not able to do the debulking (full hysterectomy). My first words were . . . *Did they?* And then I was feeling streams of tears running down my face, as I knew it was not going to be that easy. The tumors were still there. Roger was a rock. He helped me while I processed this.

At this point, I still did not know if it was cancerous or not. I just knew they were not able to do the bigger surgery. After a few moments, Roger asked if I wanted to know what they found or wait a little bit. I said no, I want to know. He said, it is stage 3C ovarian cancer.

My heart sank. Whatever stage 3C was, it was not good. Dr. Guntupalli had told us that if he were able to go in and take the tumors out, he would. The best strategy now was to do three rounds of chemo, debulking surgery (meaning remove as much tumor as possible), then three more rounds of chemo. I felt very confident in this plan and wanted to get started as soon as I could. Optionally, I could wait a bit, but I knew I wanted this out and gone as soon as possible. The very next day, I started my first chemo round. I do not want to leave you in suspense about the events after, but I will take you on that journey in my next book. Reading this will hopefully stop cancer in its tracks, and you would have no reason to read my next book.

With any medical situation you may face, having both an integrative and a traditional doctor is incredibly fortunate. For me, it was how I was able to fight every day. The two doctors worked together to give me the best treatment possible.

If you think there is something gynecological going on, do not walk, run to go see a gynecologic oncologist. If you have a caring general practitioner like I have, he or she will encourage you to. That all-burning question that you secretly do not want to ask—the question, "Could this be cancer?"—it needs to be asked. And seeing someone who specializes in just that is SO important, even if you and your primary-care doctor think it could be innocuous. Not that your doctor is not knowledgeable, or fantastic for that matter, but the gynecological oncologist is a specialist. That IS ALL THESE SPECIALISTS DO! They specialize in gynecological cancers. When it's caught early, the percentage rate of survival, I am sure, will skyrocket.

Instead of playing the speculation game, go see a gynecologic oncologist. It may be the only sure-fire way to find out the all-mighty answer, and then fashion the next plan of action. The sooner you know, the better. It may not be a question that you want to hear the answer to, but isn't it better to know than not to? Not knowing can be deadly! It is good to go see someone who can help and to know for sure. Asking the right questions to get the right answer is crucial in the healing process. I mean, how can one heal without asking the right questions to find the right people to heal and stop being sick!

Questions can be answered only if asked. *"What?!?"* Of course. It seems self-explanatory! Okay, before you close the book and call it a day, just hear me out. Of the many questions you have, finding the right ones is often the hardest. Let me see if I can explain this because understanding what questions to ask can be tricky. Relating to books is my thing. This next story handily supports my point. I am reading *Healing the Wounded King* by John Mathews, the iconic myth about searching for "The Grail." In it, the premise is that men and women alike are all wounded in some way and have the ability to restore themselves back to health. The lost soul is wounded and must find a healer. A lost soul who can be healed only if he asks the RIGHT Question, but of course he does not know what it is. Not yet anyway! As Mathews writes:

> The archetypal hero of the Grail story was Perceval. He is the one on the journey to bring healing to the wounded king. His role in the mythos of woundedness is to represent all those who seek to heal, but who are themselves wounded. He grows up in isolation in the Waste Forest and is drawn to Arthur's court after meeting with some knights. A

> simple and uncomplicated youth, he follows the advice of his mother and his knightly mentor so closely that he fails to ask the all-important question concerning the Grail and the Spear and is forced to wander the ways again until he finds his way back to the Grail Castle. This time he succeeds in bringing healing to the Wounded King. [I]

For some time, Perceval wandered, living his life, thinking that he had it all together. When he came across knights of King Arthur, he immediately longed to go the royal court at Caerleon. Before setting out, however, he returned home and told his mother of his desires. Deeply saddened, she did her best to prevent this intent. Her efforts failing, like any good mother, she gave him sound advice to carry with him. He was so desperate to be with these knights that when his mother fainted and fell as he was leaving, he did not go to her. Even though he saw her fall, the desperation to go to the royal court blinded his judgment and he rode on. He continued his journey in the same careless, disrespectful manner. His choices left him bewildered—not understanding why he was encountering problems.

Day in and day out, he still didn't know what his mistake was. Then a fisherman invited him to his house to rest. In this beautiful home he was welcomed wholeheartedly and led to a hall where he an elderly man was sitting up in a large bed. While they were talking something peculiar happened. A youth entered the room, carrying a jeweled sword made by a famous smith. The elderly man, the old lord, stated that the sword was meant for Perceval, and he personally fastened it on him. Then a boy came in with a white spear, and two more youths came in carrying two golden candlesticks. After that, a girl came in with a grail between her hands. With this came such miraculous light that the candles lost their glow. Soon afterwards, another girl came in bearing a silver platter. These artifacts were carried through the hall, past the bed where the old lord sat, and into another chamber. All the while, Perceval said nothing. After that they ate and turned in for the night. He was mystified. He wanted to ask what in the world just happened but decided to ask the servants in the morning.

When he woke, the castle was deserted, his armor laid out, with his horse saddled and ready to go. Confused, he rode away. When he came across a maiden weeping, she quickly explained that he must have spent the night in the house of the Fisher King. He assured her that he indeed stayed at a fisherman's house but in no way did he know if he was a king or not. She declared that he was indeed a king, that he spent his time fishing because of an old battle wound. She chastised Perceval for not asking about the "wanderers" (the youths from the previous night, who carried the jeweled sword, white spear, candlesticks, grail, and trencher). If he had asked about them, the Fisher King would be healed.

His silence, his lack of curiosity, not only hurt him but hurt others as well. For five years, not resting more than one night in any one destination, he searched for the Fisher King's house so he could ask about the wanderers. As the story continues to unfold, the Fisher King is actually his uncle. Perceval eventually tells him that the reason he did not ask about the wanderers was his mother's death was preying on his conscience. Percival felt great sorrow, and the Fisher King forgave him. This transformed them both, *as their wounds turned into strengths.*

This iconic story is so prevalent in my cancer journey. The awareness of my wound, my cancer, led me to ask myself the hard questions. This questioning was imperative, as it was essential to have a clear path and accept the situation as it was. To confront my diagnosis head on with nothing getting in the way spiritually, mentally, or physically. As a result, doors opened to a sequence of events. By seeking information, I had the capacity to see things from a different perspective—able to face the hard days as they evolved. Consequently, I found a healing pathway in which I owned my cancer and all challenges that came with it. The story of the Grail is miraculous, one of the most powerful healing stories ever to be told. For me, it was a reminder of my strength and that I have a choice as to how I can make changes.

A life-altering experience may be hard to understand and accept. Starting the healing process is often more painful than the path that got you to the healer, which often takes twists and turns.

I do not think it was a coincidence that I found this book as we were cleaning our storage room. It just appeared. I think it was God's way of communicating with me.

As I was reading, I had an "ah-ha" moment. It hit me like a ton of bricks. I can identify with it, am drawn to it. I too was the lost soul—like Percival seeking the Fisher King. I finally found the Wounded King and I feel that I laid down all my fears, asked the right question, and in turn found my Holy Grail in being cancer free.

I realized that I had been blindly walking through the warning signs for ovarian cancer: making excuses, convincing myself that these symptoms were normal. Perceiving with more clarity would have brought me to the doctor earlier. Most importantly, asking the right questions. For example, "Could this be cancer?" One that seems so obvious now, but that at the time I found foreign and unnecessary. Learn from me. It does not hurt to ask the hard questions, as it may save you precious time and most importantly your life!

I find stories about people who take charge of their own healing so inspirational. I know from experience that having mental, physical, and spiritual well-being is the key to my health! Not just the physical alone. As my journey progressed, reading books like *Healing the Wounded King* or *The Power of Now* by Eckhart Tolle and *Limitless* by Jim Kwik and *How to Think like a Monk* by Jay Shetty, practicing yoga, meditating, and communicating with others has led me to find my true purpose. To continue to take deep dives into the reality and meaning of life.

Without a doubt, my journey with cancer has guided me to go deeper into what my life's purpose is. To share with as many people as I can. Pass on hope, love, and guidance. These are just some of the many things that I was so fortunate to find. No matter what your question may be, I hope my story will help you find the answer—that it will help give you the courage to ask your RIGHT question and guide you on your own healing journey.

---

1. John Matthews, Healing the Wounded King, Shaftesbury, Dorset, UK: Element Books Limited (1997), 21.

Chapter 2

Awareness

> Awareness is like the sun. When it shines on things, they are transformed. —Thich Nhat Hanh

When someone asks you to reveal a bit about yourself, are you at a loss for words? I never really know what to say. Do I go with the traditional "what I do for a living," or a deeper level? Usually, it depends on who the person is. As I see it, being vulnerable, honest, and real is the way to go. It allows me to meet up close so many fascinating people. I get to have a deeper connection with others. More times than not, I learn from them! I have been known to be an oversharer. I used to think that was a bad thing, but the human connection is so strong that I feel it is important to be real with one another.

It has taken me my whole life to be where I am today. I am not the same person I was ten, fifteen, years ago. Or even yesterday, for that matter. I am constantly learning and growing with each passing day. It is not that I did not do this before, but now I am more aware. I can honestly say that I think it was a side effect of the challenges I faced during my cancer journey. It helped me dig to the core of who I am and what I am truly made of.

It has been a long road and not an easy one, at that. Like Theodore Roosevelt once said, "*Nothing in this world is worth having or doing unless it means effort, pain, difficulty . . . I have never in my life envied a human being who led an easy life. I have envied a great many people who led difficult lives and led them well.*" [1]

Having courage to be vulnerable is so powerful. I shed all the unnecessary layers I thought were there to protect me but that were just falsehoods. I do not need them anymore. I feel freer and lighter than ever. Emotions of uncertainty about the road ahead catch me off guard at times. That's okay because I am aware they are there. Being rigorously honest creates a new perspective that leads to a bright light, a light of possibility. It turns the fear into faith. Uncertainty into possibility. Despair into Hope. It puts me in the present moment, embracing the know-how to face whatever comes my way. Having this awareness is the key to a fulfilling life.

What does living the life of my highest opportunities mean? The answer was not always clear to me. I am truly grateful for everyone and everything in my life! When times get hard, those people, those activities, make me more aware. I can live my best life because I have them and they have me. By nature, I am a people person. I find strength in communities, especially if they involve healthy collaboration. Even in school, I excelled in group projects. Within the groups, I would find my strength without even knowing it.

It took me my whole life to realize that what I thought were weaknesses were many times instead doorways to my strengths. I have dyslexia. Through that path I learned my strengths are perseverance, empathy, and optimism. Persevere to never give up. Have empathy to get a deep understanding of what others are going through. And optimism to believe that no matter what, anything is possible. These strengths are some of my core values, and they became blatantly clear during my cancer journey. It was like—before cancer—God was making sure I was aware of them!

I married one of the good ones! My husband, Roger, supports me. Helps me be a better me! We have two incredible children. Our daughter, Lokela, just turned twelve and our son, Ryan, nine. We live in Fort Collins, Colorado, a wonderful place to raise a family. I am not a native Coloradoan I was born in 100 Mile House, British Columbia, Canada (elevation 1,900 feet). British Colombia (BC) is the westernmost state in Canada. It is known for its natural beauty, epic Canadian Rockies, hundreds of lakes, exceptional wilderness, and luscious cherries from the Okanagan Valley. A place I will forever hold dear in my heart. For me, hometowns are just like that. I would spend my days climbing trees, riding bikes, and making mud pies—building forts with my brother in what felt like an endless backyard. It was a safe place for a kid to explore. I wish the world were like it was back when I was a kid: wake up, go on daily adventures, and come home when it gets dark. Oh, those were the days.

My occupation changes from moment to moment as a stay-at-home mom, with tasks ranging from teacher, nurse, counselor, to chef, or all of them rolled into one. It is the best gig in town! I am forty-five years old, and I feel like I am just getting started. Taking time to grow, find my true self, make mistakes, learn from them is so rewarding.

Some days, of course, are better than others—those when I focus on grace, love, and peace, a direct result of being a cancer survivor. Also, a fighter who will forever be grateful for my journey. Having cancer gave me a clarity. The ability to see things from a different lens. Facing ovarian cancer forced me to not worry about the little things but acknowledge what really matters. For me, that is family, life, and attitude. I am fortunate enough to be able to open this gift every day! A happy life, full of adventure!

In 1985, my family moved down to North Texas. I was nearly ten. It was a huge culture shock. Going from a small town of about a thousand inhabitants to a big city like Dallas brought inevitable change. Even though I missed living in Canada, North Texas was where we needed to be for work-related reasons. We intended to stay only a couple of years. Leaving our dog Mandy behind, we rented a room in a home-office building for storage, packed all our essentials, put them in a truck extended cab, and drove down to our new home. Both my brother and I got to pack one 18 x 18 x 24 box with all we wanted to bring with us. My box was mostly filled with stuffed animals.

For all you dog lovers, we had a friend bring Mandy down, once we knew were not moving back. Oh, how we missed her terribly and were so extremely happy when she was living with us again.

The move gave us so many opportunities that we would not have had, living back in 100 Mile House. My heart will always and forever be Canadian, even after thirty years of living in the States. People often ask where I am from. When I tell them Canada, they say, "Oh yes, that makes sense." Being a Canadian is part of me, and why I am the way I am. As the years passed, my brother moved back there, and my parents ended up relocating in New Mexico. At some point, I decided I wanted my mountains again. I remember driving to work one day. The smog and haze had replaced my mountains. Not in any way comparable to the real thing. It was not too long after that I upped and moved to Fort Collins. It felt like home the moment I arrived.

Roger is an engineer by trade. Since 2008, a year before Kela was born—thinking years down the road to set us up for our future—he has been investing in houses.

I am truly appreciative of the time and effort he has put into the real-estate business, which has paid off nicely. When I read books, I often wonder where the story first began. This one started after reading a book. Go figure! He read, *Rich Dad, Poor Dad* by Robert Kiyosaki. From that moment, he started investing. This has led to incredible advantages. I am able to continue to be a stay-at-home mom, which I absolutely love! In addition, we can still have our same lifestyle. Most importantly, he was able to go part-time as an engineer, giving him extra time at home—thus, strengthening all our relationships. Especially with the kids. With Kela, he gets to do fun projects that she dreams up. For Ryan, he used to ask every single morning if his daddy had to go to work. When Roger would say, "Yes, Buddy," our son's little heart would be absolutely crushed. He tried not to show it, as being quite empathetic, he knew it was hard on Roger. The time he gets to spend with us is priceless!

Roger has always been a hands-on dad. More time at home was just the icing on the cake. Going part-time as an engineer worked out especially well on vacations. We had always gone here and there, doing summer fun activities. He was often unable to participate, being, of course, at the office. Roger would tell me he was jealous because when he was headed to work, we were heading to the pool. By going part-time, he was able to be there for swimming, biking, and just plain old summer fun! Even if we went nowhere, it always felt like a mini vacation, as we were all together creating memories.

There were so many moving parts with the diagnosis. Knowing that he did not have to work full time reduced the worries. He did not need to take time off his engineering job to be by my side during my cancer treatments. These moments along with so many others will be in my next book. The most important thing to know now is, he was there, through and through! Nothing would have kept him from it. It was just a non-issue; his boss knew what was happening and was very supportive. One thing from the moment I met Roger is, he has always been there! It's one of the many reasons I love him so much!

The ovarian-cancer protocol went as planned. We threw everything at this cancer, and I responded well to it all. I had decided I would start intermittent fasting, in addition to eating a ketogenic diet. The books I read stated that this helps with the chemo. The fasting plus not feeding the cancer sugar was giving the chemo magic superpowers. I envisioned the chemo had a magic wand that zapped all the cancer cells that just chemo alone would have missed. With each infusion, my numbers drastically dropped. By February of my last chemo my numbers were fantastic.

I was getting my energy back. I had no signs of cancer. My CA-125 was a 10. Remember, when I started out, it was 734 and rose to 1235! And there was an oral chemo medication I could take now to help me stay at a safe level. As time passed, every couple of months I had my blood work taken to ensure that my CA-125 was *still under 35*. Each time I got my blood work done, my number had crept up. Meaning at the last day of my chemo in February 2020 my CA-125 was 10; each month thereafter, it went up a couple of numbers, and by November 2020 it was at 17. Nothing alarming, just something to keep an eye on. So, all in all, things were going very well!

By November 2020, I had been in remission for nine months. My old self seemed to be showing herself again. Not quite where I wanted to be, but enough. One evening Roger and I were talking about our future. This past year had been a huge eye opener for us, helping us think outside the box. What things were we doing that are working, and what did we want our future to look like? He asked me if I would be interested in learning more about the business.

Roger has always thought ahead. Planning for our future had been a core virtue of his, even before we met. He learns from the past, putting in the work today for a better tomorrow. I live more in the now. That makes us a good team. We balance each other out. I help him enjoy life in the moment, and he helps me be ready for future endeavors. My cancer threw a curve ball into the mix. Rightfully so. Thankfully, we stopped this cancer in its tracks, and I was recovering nicely. Once again, our future together was bright.

Roger had always been vocal that he would be the one to "go" before me, and at this point, he thought: *Okay, now that we are back on track, I want you to know a bit about the business just in case something happens to me*. This is where I check out. I change the subject, because in my magical crystal ball, I know that will not happen. My vision of our future always has us together, no matter what!

This life-altering conversation about our future took place right in the middle of the pandemic. The roller coaster of chemo and doctor appointments was at a slow crawl. Instead of meeting the doctor every three weeks, it was every three months. In lockdown, our lives had taken a bit of a turn but nothing drastic. Obviously, my immune system was low, and we needed to take extra precautions surrounding that new risk factor. We just had to pivot a bit. Roll with the change the best way we knew how. We followed the recommended protocol. We were safe, but we also lived our lives.

With my background as a former elementary-school teacher, I had the expertise to help my kids through this new virtual-school reality. My role at home just got kicked up a notch. I was excited. The hardest part was that they did not have the social interaction they craved. It was a learning curve that was tough, but manageable. I was so happy that they had each other. Once we established a routine, we got the hang of it. With our family unit, the forced change brought us all closer and opened opportunities that would not have been there otherwise. Some habits we continue today is we all take a walk first thing in the morning and read together before bed.

I honestly did not know how to answer his question about wanting to be more involved in the business. I could not wrap my head around how I would find the time to learn more about his work. He had always appreciated that I do everything at home: groceries, cleaning, laundry, kids, etc. So he can spend the time growing the business. I knew this question was important to him. I really thought about it. Time is such a precious commodity. I did not know where I could fit it in without dropping all the spinning plates I had going. I pondered. If it mattered to him, it mattered to me. I thought of a solution. I listen to podcasts. I could add one into my mix. Just make it a priority.

I asked Roger to send me a podcast he thought would be beneficial. He sent one I related to in so many ways. It was a podcast to help with goals to grow the business, in addition to life. As it turned out, it was promoting a class for couples: The ONE Thing Goal Setting Retreat—led by Geoff Woods and Jay Papasan, the authors of *The ONE Thing*. This workshop came at an opportune time, as I was in remission, feeling good. It gave me a focus. For the past year or so, my energy had been dedicated to getting healthy. Now it was geared towards staying healthy. That included living my best life. This retreat was just the ticket. It intrigued me. The timing was ripe for me to start this new chapter in my life.

Being diagnosed with such a life-threatening disease and coming out the other side cancer free made me reflect on my core values. I had so many. The retreat helped narrow them down to three: health, optimism, and balance. That does not mean that I do not have other values. These three just make things in my life easier or unnecessary. It is a moto I learned through *The ONE Thing*—a constant Geoff and Jay ask throughout the book and in the retreat: "What's the one thing I can do such that by doing it everything else will be easier or unnecessary?"

When I am healthy, I am not using my energy to get healthy. When I find balance, I find peace. This leads to a life with little-to-no stress. When I am optimistic, I see things in a more positive perspective—that no matter what comes my way, it will all be okay. These values are what drive me every day. Geoff and Jay, in the workshop, coached us on how we can live a better life by doing small tasks that will create and reach life goals. In addition, , it incorporated ways for our relationships to support our goals as a couple.

These deep-dive discussions strengthened our affection for each other. We had to be vulnerable with each other, which supported the flow of intimacy and intentionality that already existed in our marriage, just making it stronger. It was a win, win all the way around. We made our *someday goals* for ourselves. Goals that came from discovering our personal core beliefs. This workshop ignited a plan to start the ball rolling, encouraging us to take action steps to an even happier future with each other.

What exactly is *a someday goal*? It is a dream that is so big that in the present time it seems impossible, but with specific priorities each day the dream becomes attainable. Nothing is off the table. The bigger the goal, the better! It gave me permission to dream big.

So, I started thinking about what would be on my someday list. Travel the world, be disease free, have time for twenty dates with Roger and twenty with extended family, per year, have a mother/daughter art studio, and write this book. I had just ten minutes to write something down when that thought came. I put it aside, letting it sink in. The seed started growing. Could I write a book? No, was my first reaction, but just a small glimpse of possibility led me to believe I could do it. That small window of opportunity, I grabbed onto. With a little willingness and confidence, it started growing. My thoughts motivated me to focus on the importance of how cancer can be a life-altering experience. An experience that can go one of two ways. Negative or positive. The diagnosis will not change. How it is handled can.

In addition, how critical it is to know the common early signs of ovarian cancer. Knowing the B.A.S.I.I.C.S. Not only knowing but accepting this disease with a positive perspective and mindset. In my experience, they were just as important as the traditional cancer therapies.

I did not have any desire to write a book before. I wrote a kids' book once, but just for a college class. I enjoyed writing it and shared what I wrote with kids, family, and close friends, but did not take it further. Having dyslexia, I was always forced to read. I did not read for pleasure until I was twenty-seven. I might read one book a year, at best, till one day I discovered my genre—finally figured out what books I liked reading: autobiographies, especially about transformative experiences. One day at my parents' place, looking at their selection, I saw *Angela's Ashes*, by Frank McCourt, a Pulitzer Prize–winning, # 1 *New York Times* bestseller, billed on Amazon as "Frank McCourt's masterful memoir of his childhood in Ireland." Frank McCourt was born in Brooklyn in 1930 and when he was four moved to the slums of Limerick, Ireland. He had a childhood filled with deprivation, humor, and adventure, or, as the Amazon description put it, "wearing rags for diapers, begging a pig's head for Christmas dinner and gathering coal from the roadside to light a fire."

His father consumed his wages in alcohol, and after the death of Frank's baby sister, his mother sank into depression. However, his father was a storyteller. His stories earned him Frank's affection and love. Hospitalized for months with typhoid, Frank again took comfort in stories, discovering his talent for language. In this way, he made the best out of a very detrimental situation. What an amazing life, just incredible. I feel on some level I can identify with him; that is, in the way he turned negatives into positives.

Even on my lowest days, I tried to put one foot in front of the other. I, like Frank, made the best out of a very painful situation. Having cancer is something I do not ever wish on anyone! Having chemotherapy every three weeks—it zapped everything out of me. Some days, I could walk my kids to school, which was a quarter mile away. On the way back, barely make it back. On other days. just going to the bathroom was almost too taxing. Then as soon as I started feeling better, it was time to get another infusion. I came up with a moto: "I will go when I can and rest when I need to."

To surrender to my limitations was very humbling. That does not mean I gave in easily. My family would urge me to sit and rest. I gave them my word I would not overdo it. In the meantime, I had to keep moving.

A day after I found out I had cancer, Amy came into my world. She is another incredible ovarian-cancer survivor. Amy told me she walked every single day during her treatments. This was always in the forefront of my mind—my inspiration in keeping moving, even if it was one block or in my case to the bathroom and back. Having the awareness to know when I needed to rest was a great balancing act. Rest was necessary as part of my treatments and therapies. But as hard as it was, walking helped me physically and mentally.

Writing my memoir was much bigger than me. Somewhere, the universe was directing me to do it. Listening to that voice is how this book came to be. I knew without a shadow of a doubt that I had to share my story. I hope it will inspire you. To listen to your body, find the right doctors, and go get checked. It can truly save your life!

---

1. Quoted by Sherre Hirsch to open Chapter 1, Thresholds: How to Thrive Through Life's Transitions to Live Fearlessly and Regret-Free.

Chapter 3

Purpose

> If you have a strong purpose in life, you don't have to be pushed, your passion will drive you there. — Roy T. Bennett

Have you ever read the *Sesame Street* kids' book *Monster at the End of This Book (starring lovable, furry old Grover)* by Jon Stone, with Mike Smollin as illustrator?

It's a classic! If you haven't, then you should put this one down and check it out. It is one of those books I remember reading over and over as a kid. Besides being so memorable, it's quite humorous. My kids asked me to read it over and over, and over again too! The star character, Grover, is a sweet, furry, lovable blue monster, who spends the entire book trying to persuade the reader not to turn the pages. He does not want you to get to the end. He comes up with some inventive ways to encourage you not to. This is solely because of the title, which plainly states that there's a monster at the end. He does not know it will be him. So, he pleads profusely not to turn the pages. It's understandable, as he fears the unknown.

The reader just keeps turning and turning the pages because when humans are told not to do something, they usually do the opposite. He kind of loses it in the middle. I think deep down, he is really frightened of meeting that monster. He knows it is there and is terrified. Finally, at the end, it's not at all as bad as he was making it out to be. In the end, it was all okay! it was just lovable, furry old Grover.

It was a beautiful spring morning in April, and I decided to go for a run. I am in my own world, listening to Rich Roll, the vegan ultra-endurance athlete, my favorite podcast. And this story of Grover popped into my head. I remember thinking: *Oh, how silly.* I just carried on with my run.

The more I thought about it, though, the more it made sense. At home I immediately shared my idea with Roger. He looked at me like I was nuts. That's okay because I knew I had an idea that would make approaching cancer not so scary. His is a kids' book with a relatable *Sesame Street* character that everyone adores. Even Grover has fears and does not want to confront the inevitable monster at the end of the book. In my book, Grover's monster would be cancer.

Teaching kindergarten, before becoming a stay-at-home mom, gave me an appreciation of how important stories are. One of the reasons I started teaching was to help kids develop a love for literacy, which I had missed as a child. Once that love is snuffed out, it is hard to get back. Stories from all walks of life can help kids and adults alike relate to life events.

I would go into a bookstore or library and be in my glory, especially in the kids' section. I have a weak spot for kids' books. Even now when we go to the library, we walk out with forty to fifty books every week! No exaggeration. Even with three bags of books that we can hardly carry, we are still looking at the bookshelf to see what else we can cram into our library book bags. Reading is one of my favorite things to do with the kids. Children's stories are an incredible resource for anything and everything you may be interested in. I especially like the metaphors, which enforce the book's message. Not only learn from it but also incorporate it into my life. Books are made to be self-help, not shelf help. It is up to me to make them come to life.

Writing my story was no longer a *someday* goal. It was happening now and taking off like wildfire. The more I spent time on it, the more passionate I became. It was obvious that this, writing my story, right now was my purpose. Ideas for the book would pop up in my mind constantly. I knew I had to have a plan. A way to make writing a book attainable and not so overwhelming.

In the beginning of 2021, I started looking into how to publish books. It found Self-Publishing School through Hal Elrod, author of *The Miracle Morning: The Not-So-Obvious Secret Guaranteed to Transform Your Life (Before 8 AM)* at the end of February. I started working with my writing coach, Kerk Murray, on April 5, 2021. It was like going back to college with a major in how-to self-publish books. Their step-by-step process launched me on my way. Things started to become real and not a dream. This was happening! I did my homework, one task per day. Before I knew it, the floodgates opened, and my book was materializing before my eyes.

My knowledge of cancer was miniscule in 2019. Not knowing something can be overwhelming as information starts roaring in at a fast rate. It is almost like drinking from a water hose. So much information, not to mention that just hearing the word is scary. Or is it? I didn't know too much about it. The only knowledge I had was from people I knew who had cancer. In turn, learning through their experience. Come to think of it, not too many people in my life have survived their fight. Recognizing this, I was sure deep down that if I was going to survive this disease (and I was), I needed to stay clear of the fear. Have faith in what was trying to happen. Each day. In every moment. It was like I was the captain of a ship. Why would I stay in the murky waters? They are cold, dark, and wet.

I was the captain, and I could steer into the great wide clear beautiful ocean. I could do something about the situation. My response to this newness in my life was paramount. As a result, everything and anything that came my way, I conquered. We could not have asked for a better outcome, doctors included.

I had to embrace my diagnosis! Accepting it freed me from worry. I could use the extra positive energy to fight it. There was no way I could change the situation. However, I did have control of my perception. Especially, my attitude. At first, I, like Grover, instinctively tried to stop what was happening. Hiding from the reality, I would have missed the experience. Also, more importantly, not have survived it. Tackling it consciously with purpose got me through. My life has been filled with challenges; that is how I grow. Hiding from cancer was not a solution. I needed to learn the lesson the universe was so desperately trying to tell me.

There were many questions my inner voice wondered: *Why is this happening? How could I have avoided this? What did I do wrong?* These questions did not get me anywhere. When I accepted my diagnosis, things got better. Day by day, the solutions were more attainable! My purpose, my "ONE thing" at that point, was to do anything to stay alive! I needed to stop this cancer in its tracks. I took advice from everyone. The more the better. My oncologist, integrative doctor, Roger, family, and even my gut.

This journey gave me strength. With that strength came purpose. I embraced it the only way I knew how. I had to dig deep, analyze my current situation, and decide what path to choose. I had to make a realistic decision, one that did not require rainbows and unicorns. It all became so clear to me. Because it was a path that was familiarity. A path I had been walking on my whole life. My purposeful path is lined with optimism, perseverance, and love. There were, of course, furry moments. That, of course, was inevitable, but they didn't take over my spirit.

No matter what, *I knew* it was all going to be okay. I told myself so. With the newfound knowledge I was receiving and once we had a plan, it put my mind at peace! No matter what happened, I was in charge of my healing. I was never alone in this fight! Not ever! I did not let cancer be my identity, nor did I let it control me. My "cancer" diagnosis did not take over my mindset. *That was mine!* With that courage, I have the power to make anything possible.

I was only going to write one book. One and done. It would be split up into three parts: Part 1: Before the diagnosis. Part 2: During the cancer therapies. Part 3: Remission. But how bland. During my coaching sessions, Kerk helped me narrow down my "why." The driving force as to why I wanted to write my cancer story! As we were talking, the initial structure unraveled as my intent became transparent! My "why," my purpose, is to encourage women to go see a doctor and get checked! Know the B.A.S.I.I.C.S., the signs of ovarian cancer, and spread that information to others.

There is an Eastern saying: "The teacher and the student together create the teaching." [1] Raise ovarian-cancer awareness by teaching the B.A.S.I.I.C.S. This disease is killing too many of our mothers, daughters, aunts, grandmas, and friends. My purpose is to get to cancer before it gets to you!

Ovarian cancer a difficult disease to catch early. It is like it waves a red flag and says, "Yoo-hoo, over here!" But the symptoms do not really start until the later stages. That is why it is so critical to check things as soon as you start feeling or seeing the symptoms.

I do not blame anyone in the slightest! I feel it needs to be said, because despite the best intentions and the BEST doctors, even with an annual wellness check-up, we missed it. Doctors have so much experience in their field. Mine, Dr. Fields, surprises me every visit. I feel like I am an apprentice learning from a great and wise teacher. Really, I do not think there is anything she does not know. I know that is a bold statement, but despite being my doctor for almost two decades, she continues to pull rabbits out of her hat. Dr. Fields is humble enough to say it if she does not have an answer. That does not happen often, but if it does, she will do her best to find it. If she does not know, then she will stop at nothing to find a solution.

Without skipping a beat, my doctors knew exactly what to do. There was no lag time.

It takes comradery from all sides. A dynamo team! The universe put my doctors in my life to save me! I know this with everything in me. Anyone else, any other time, this would be a very different story! I will forever be grateful!

If I had waited a month, or even one more week, it would have inevitably progressed to stage 4. Dr. Guntupalli sees it all the time. Patients coming to him in the late stages. Women who have been seeing doctors about their concerns for up to a year or more—who find their cancer early—have a more successful outcome. They do not have to be looking into the eyes of an oncologist, wondering how much longer they have.

This shift of awareness can happen one healing story at a time. I can't cure cancer, or stop it, but I can learn more about it, and share. I heard someone say this once: "I am the expert of my own story!" That is all I know. I have been very fortunate and want to pass that fortune on to you. I hope it encourages you to see the RIGHT doctor before it is too late.

When I was first diagnosed, I thought, "Wouldn't it be great if I could just skate by without anyone knowing?" Oh, how wrong I was! The most powerful thing I could do is share with anyone who would listen. I am so grateful that person is you!

It is a privilege and honor to advocate for ovarian-cancer awareness. Your choice to get checked out will be the most courageous step you may ever have to take in your life. My suggestion is to read this with an open mind. It means that you are willing to learn more. Remember, knowledge with action brings power. Get in the driver's seat! Take action even though it seems scary and overwhelming at times. Embrace the next phase one step at a time, one moment at a time. Please learn from my experience and share it with others. It just may save your life.

---

1. Tolle, The Power of Now, Canada: Namaste Publishing Inc.,1997.

Chapter 4

Go Get Checked!

How to GET CHECKED?

This is where you need to really pay attention to the B.A.S.I.I.C.S. From all accounts I've read, it is difficult to detect ovarian cancer in the early stages. To that point, healthline.com listed these important points below in August 2021:

> Doctors often don't find ovarian cancer until it has progressed to an advanced stage. In fact, only 20 percent of ovarian cancer is diagnosed in early stages. Early-stage tumors are easier to treat and even cure. However, many ovarian cancers are not found until stages 3 and 4, at which point the cancer has spread within the pelvic region—and sometimes beyond.

> Late detection puts many people diagnosed with ovarian cancer at a disadvantage because of how quickly it has spread by this time. [1]

That is because the cancer is on the inside of our bodies and does not truly show itself until symptoms start becoming more severe. The more the cancer grows, the stronger the symptoms. So, it is important you know what is happening in your body. That is not to say you need all the symptoms before getting checked. But if you have even one, go get checked. Find the right doctor. Ask for a CA125 (cancer antigen) test. Get an ultrasound. Get a CT scan. Anything to have your questions—and concerns—addressed.

Do not leave until you get all your concerns and questions answered. Even if they seem trivial and nonthreatening. Like my mom has always told me, it does not hurt to ask. What's the worst thing that could happen? Get a couple of tests done. Then if and only if it is cancer, finding out early can save your life. If not, then you know. Be grateful, of course, and carry on with a new perspective. If your path takes you in another direction, having that knowledge will give you a plan of action.

Again, knowledge with action is power. This is where the rubber meets the road. Use this as a driving force to start your healing!

Throughout this entire process, my greatest strengths came out in so many ways. I have always been one that just goes with the flow. Whatever happens, happens! It is what it is. When life throws me a curve, I just deal with it. No matter what the circumstances are. When I got the news about my cancer, I already knew that I couldn't do anything about it. It is what it is, right?

No! Not so much. I had one of those deep God-gut thoughts. I couldn't change the diagnosis that autumn day in 2019. But sure as fire, I knew that I could change how I responded! The magic to all of this was my attitude. As a result, I quickly went into remission and plan to be in remission for a very long time.

As with any healing journey, it is so important that you know you are not alone. The universe has its way of balancing things out. In one of my virtual yoga sessions my yoga instructor said, "The universe is forming so that people in the universe can be formed" (*Yoga with Adriene Mishler*—YouTube). [2]

I am so blessed to have the best and most incredible tribe ever! They were and still are the pinnacle part of my recovery! Amazing people who were with me every step of the way.

My support system helped me focus on the reality of the situation. Gingerly, they were trying to help me wrap my head around how serious this was; I could not pretend it away but had to focus on what really matters and listen to what the universe was telling me.

Universe: "Your true strength comes from your genuine acceptance. You will not survive this if you try to go about it alone! We got you! So, just sit this one out and focus your energy on healing!"

Funny thing was, that was one of the hardest things I had to do. My first action step after my diagnosis was *un*-volunteering. This seemed so simple but wasn't. I did not want to *un*-volunteer but had to. Being very involved in my kids' school, I had just signed up to be a room mom. At first, I assured my son's teacher I could still play that role. I truly believed this. Had I not meant it, I would not have said it. Understanding what a hard time I often had saying no, a friend, one of the kindest people I know, stepped in. She suggested that we could be co-room moms. She would take over. In the meantime, if she needed anythinց
am guessing you know what happened
right. She knew before I knew that this
energy and there would be no room for
time!

I had no idea what was coming down the pike. I thought I had some inclination. Not by a long shot! During my treatments, I got a heavy dose of humility. I kept telling myself: *This is not forever. This is temporary. I will soon be able to get back to my life and do all the things I've always done.* That was not healthy, as I was living in the future and not in the present.

Knowing how to be in the present helped me realize that I should not worry about what lies ahead—cancer or no cancer. That is too much to take on. And not very practical—as most of the things that bring on worry do not ever happen. Every time I would start going into the "what if" world, I would stop myself. And look at what I could do in that moment to stay present. Like breathing, reading, or just talking to someone about how I was feeling. Having a task list helped, as I would focus on doing one thing a day. This list was not fancy by any means: take a shower, go for a walk, read with my kids, make a meal. These little tasks helped me keep myself from totally falling apart. In addition, I did not want the worry to live rent free in my head. That space, I needed for encouraging helpful thoughts! I especially did not want the worry thoughts to come to fruition.

Being *in the now* gave me focus to be worry free! I became very conscious of this NOW and how beneficial it was. For weeks, I had avoided reality, not knowing it—trying to do all the things I'd been doing before the diagnosis. *If I could keep up my routine, then it was easy to pretend I did not have cancer.* Acceptance, not avoidance, was the key for my success. Moving into a state of acceptance was incredibly powerful. It gave me the spiritual enlightenment to fight this with all I had!

As time passed, people would ask . . . in a kind of singsong, high-pitched voice, "How are you?" "How are you feeling?"—with the sympathetic head tilt. I am sure I used to behave the same [illegible] talking with people who had cancer. I could even recognize [illegible]mmiseration over the phone. It was hard at first, but it also [illegible]eat deal to know how much they cared!

Being on the other side of the fence was very difficult to accept. Meaning, I was the one who was sick, instead of being a caregiver. Never in a million years did I ever think that I would be on the other side. Yet there I was, it was me. I was the one who was fighting for my life. Accepting this help meant I had to accept my cancer, and everything that came with it. I had to surrender to the fact that I had it, and there was not a darn thing I could do about it.

There were rare moments when I was in tears without any warning. I would be having a conversation. My mind jumped to associate how I felt when making dinner or running an errand for someone. Then all of a sudden *bam*, the waterworks started falling. Truthfully, I so badly wanted to be in *that* role instead of the one I was currently in. The flood of emotions was just so overwhelming.

It was not only the fact that I had cancer that got me. It was the vulnerability of it all: coming to the realization that it was my turn to let the universe help me. I just never thought that it would be me. Good thing I am not in charge. God had other plans. I needed to be present to know what they were. It was God's way for me to learn something. Part of me was thinking: *Okay, God! Thank you, but I'm good. Nothing I need to learn down here. Just keep moving along!* Had it happened that way, then there would have been a lifetime of lessons I missed. I am blessed to be along for this beautiful ride we call life. The lessons are continuous, and I am constantly learning. My wish is for you to be willing, open, and honest. Listen to what the universe is trying to tell you! When I did this for myself, things changed. What could very well have been tragic turned into triumph!

---

1. Kimberly Holland, "Ovarian Cancer Is Difficult to Diagnose—Here's Why," National Ovarian Cancer Coalition, https://www.healthline.com/health/ovarian-cancer/how-a-diagnosis-is-determined.
2. "Yoga with Adriene," https://www.youtube.com/user/yogawithadriene.

Chapter 5

Symptoms

> If you don't ask, the answer is always no. If you don't go after what you want, you'll never have it. If you don't step forward, you will always stay in the same spot. — Nora Roberts

> And if you don't listen to your body, you could face a deadly outcome! — Trish Kifer

This chapter consists of research I found to be informational. I wanted to get you correct information on the all-important symptoms from another source than myself. So, I drew from a couple of outstanding medical facilities—which had similar data.

Below is important information taken from the "Ask the Expert" series on the Memorial Sloan Keating Cancer Center website. This issue features gynecologic surgeon Dennis Chi in "Why Don't We Screen More Women for Ovarian Cancer?" [1]

Advances in detection:

There is currently much research focused on ways to better detect ovarian cancer at an early stage. Many centers, including Memorial Sloan Kettering, are looking for biomarkers in the blood that are more accurate than CA-125 at indicating early-stage disease or even precancerous conditions.

Additionally, research in recent years has shed light on the possible origins of ovarian cancer. "Many studies have suggested that ovarian cancers may start in the fallopian tubes rather than the ovaries," Dr. Chi explains. "If this hypothesis proves to be correct, it may allow us to develop better imaging methods and more-accurate screening tests."

"One of the reasons it's so hard to detect ovarian cancer at an early stage is because ovaries are inside your body where small lumps cannot be felt," Dr. Chi says. Common symptoms of the disease—such as nausea, pelvic pressure, urinary or gastrointestinal symptoms, or pain—can be caused by many conditions that are not ovarian cancer.

"If you had several of these symptoms together for a duration of time greater than a few months, it's probably a good idea to see your gynecologist," he concludes. "He or she may recommend an ultrasound or a CA-125 test or possibly a CT scan."

The Division of Gynecologic Oncology at the University of Colorado:

Below I quote from their website. Dedicated to women's cancer, they report that "Early ovarian cancer typically presents itself in the following common symptoms" [2]

- *Persistent bloating*
- *Acid reflux and Indigestion*

- *Constant pain in the abdomen*
- *Abnormal uterine bleeding*
- *Feeling full quickly or difficulty eating*
- *Pain in the abdomen during sexual intercourse*

Compare this to Memorial Sloan Kettering, who tells us:

> *Although the symptoms of ovarian cancer may be vague, particularly in the early stages, they are usually fairly constant and represent a change from how you normally feel. Symptoms also worsen as the cancer progresses.*

Memorial *Sloa*n Kettering Cancer Center's list of symptoms of ovarian cancer is a little longer. [3]

- Abdominal bloating or swelling
- Pain in the abdomen or pelvis
- Difficulty eating, or feeling full quickly
- Lack of appetite
- Feeling an urgent need to urinate
- Needing to urinate frequently
- Change in bowel habits (constipation or diarrhea)
- Change in menstrual periods
- Vaginal bleeding between periods
- Back pain

- Weight gain or loss

My personal ovarian-cancer symptoms included (not on the list above):

- Tiredness
- Irregular periods
- Weakness (not as strong as I should have been)

It is so critical that you know the early symptoms for ovarian cancer. My husband and I came up with an easy to remember acronym with the seven most common symptoms. They are the foundation for the title for this book.

Knowing the B.A.S.I.I.C.S.

B = **B**loating
A = **A**bnormal blood in the urin
S = **S**tomach full quickly (or having difficulty in eating)
C = **C**onstant pain in abdomen
I = **I**ndigestion and acid reflux
I = **I**ncontinence (needing to urinate frequently)
S = **S**ex is painful

I listed so many ovarian cancer symptoms, as it is important to be familiar with them all. The symptoms are imperative, as they are what gets you to a doctor. The B.A.S.I.I.C.S. are the main ones. It is crucial to recognize them without having to think about it. When they show up, you just know, and in turn you know what to do next. The B.A.S.I.I.C.S. are the biggies, and if you have one or more, I recommend going to see an ovarian-cancer expert.

The symptom that got me to the doctor, and the one that saved my life, was "Sex is painful." I had pain in my abdomen during sexual intercourse. Even then, I almost waited too long.

We would have caught the cancer earlier if I had just taken time to think long and hard about my symptoms. Not been so dismissive, thinking I knew what they were. If I had listened to my body, really listened. It was way easier to explain away these symptoms. It is not like I did not reflect on them. But I always came up with a legit reason why I was having issues. There were so many explanations for why cancer was not ever addressed. It was also the furthest thing from any of our minds.

There are myriads of reasons people get cancer. None of which I am an expert in, in any way. I do have an incredible book that I read after I was first diagnosed. A must read! My integrative doctor, Dr. Fields, recommended *The Metabolic Approach to Cancer: Integrating Deep Nutrition, the Ketogenic Diet, and Nontoxic Bio-Individualized Therapies*, by Dr. Nasha Winters, an inspirational story of another cancer survivor. This book made so much sense to me. It helped me with the day-to-day challenges. Most importantly, it was a learning guide in the way I approached my cancer diagnosis. My attitude set the tone for everything. My healing mindset was a feeling rooted into my soul. I knew that following the advice and teachings from the book, I was going to make it. Not only to make it, but to stay in remission so I can be here to fulfill my life's purpose.

Stop, look, and listen to that voice inside you! Be the hero of your own story and take charge of your own health! Just like any of us, doctors are human and have a passion to keep us alive. Doing things as a team will create a much better outcome in any situation. The doctor/patient duo is a team. They need us to let them know what is truly happening. This requires rigorous inventory on our part, so they know how to do their best to help. Doctors have the expertise, experience, skill, and knowledge. You do too, but on a different level. Collaboration is the key. A strong bridge between the patient and the doctor is a necessity. It is my hope that I can help build that bridge.

I believe that is why so many people share their stories. There is so much information out there. Digital deluge is hurting us as much as it is helping. So much information that it is hard for any of us to absorb it all. The more research I did, the more I understood what I had to do. The steps to take to kick this cancer from my body for good! Knowledge I learned and applied to my treatments saved my life! You deserve the best! Take the time to find the right doctor. Get valid information. This will lead you in the right direction. I have the fortune of being able to live my life each day to the fullest. Instead of spending each day hurting and fighting for my life.

Getting the symptoms checked out and finding out early is a matter of life and death. I will say it again and again throughout the book. Go see a doctor if you have any of the common signs. When you remember the B.A.S.I.I.C.S. it can save your life!

In *Sex and Cancer*, Dr. S. Guntupalli wisely states:

"Waiting is Suicidal."

---

1. Julie Grisham, "Why Don't We Screen More Women for Ovarian Cancer?" September 2013, Memorial Sloan Kettering Cancer Center, https://www.mskcc.org/news/why-don-t-we-screen-more-women-ovarian.
2. The Division of Gynecologic Oncology at the University of Colorado,
3. Memorial Sloan Kettering Cancer Center — "Signs & Symptoms of Ovarian Cancer," https://www.mskcc.org/cancer-care/types/ovarian/symptoms.

Chapter 6

Myth # 1

How could I have Ovarian Cancer? . . . I'm too Young!

> The good thing about being young is you are not experienced enough to know you cannot possibly do the things you are doing. — Unknown

No matter what other people tell you, you are as old as your heart makes you out to be. Being in your forties is not old. Being in your sixties, seventies, and eighties is not old, either. I thought that when I got to an advanced age, I might have some medical issue in one form or another. From what I hear, that is just what happens when we get older. So, being forty-three years old and having stage 3C ovarian cancer was a bit of a shocker.

I hear it all the time. *Oh, I am so old!* I am sure you have heard or may even have said it yourself. I remember, when I was about fourteen, having a conversation with my grandma Bunny. She said, "You can call me old when I am one hundred and fifteen years old, and even then, when I get to a hundred fifteen, I'm going to count backwards." Wisdom from a true soul. She had the kindest heart in all the world. Being young at heart is something she taught me, and I am so blessed to be able to pass that on to my kids.

It was atypical to have ovarian cancer at the age of forty-three. Meaning it is uncommon for anyone under fifty. But not impossible. It does happen. No matter how old you are, still pay attention to the B.A.S.I.I.C.S. In short, that I was young did not mean squat!

> *Postmenopausal women, most commonly in their 60s to 70s, are affected by the most common types of ovarian, fallopian, and peritoneal cancers. I will refer to these cancers as ovarian cancers. In the United States, it is the second most common gynecologic cancer after uterine cancer. The average lifetime risk of being diagnosed with ovarian cancer is about 1 to 2 percent. There are hereditary forms of ovarian cancer where women develop cancer at a younger age in their 40s to 50s.* [1]

MY SNEAKY OVARIAN-CANCER SYMPTOMS THAT APPEARED AS AGE-RELATED SYMPTOMS . . . SLEEP, INCONTINENCE, PAIN IN ABDOMEN

SLEEP

Are you tired? For many of us, the answer is invariably "Yes!" Currently, people are going with their hair on fire. I try not to be that busy. I told myself if I must write it on a calendar, then I am too busy. I did not want to have a calendar that looked like it would take a rocket scientist to understand. As it turns out, writing on my calendar helped me keep things in order. It was simple. The way I liked it. It helped me not get overwhelmed. In addition, I wasn't running around with my hair on fire. A couple months before my diagnosis, I was feeling tired. I just thought it was normal. Lots of people are tired with the day-to-day activities. Being tired was a totally legit symptom that had no red flags concerning cancer.

One explanation of being tired was that I have two kids! Being tired is just a part of parenting. Come to think of it, I haven't really slept through the night in over nine years. My daughter Kela was born in 2010, and at that time I was nursing her and getting up for her at night. My son was on the way. At seven months old, Ryan had respiratory syncytial virus (RSV). It is a viral illness where it is difficult for the babies to breathe. He spent a week in the pediatric ICU. He was seven years old by the time he was sleeping through the night.

Ever since being in ICU, he's been a little restless, and not a very good sleeper. We feel that the time he spent in the hospital really affected him. I truly never once minded when he woke me up. Making sure the kids feel safe and loved has always been of utmost importance to me. I never let my kids cry themselves to sleep, even against the advice of other expert parents! I just couldn't do it. I wanted my kids to know that we will always be there for them, no matter what.

As he got older, I would have to sleep next to him, holding his hand until he fell asleep. As time went on, I graduated to the hall. He would still wake up and ask, "Mom, are you there?" "Yup!" Then one night, sitting in the hall, I remember looking up and seeing a nice comfy chair. What the heck am I doing sitting on the floor when I can get into the nice comfy chair? Oh, how my butt appreciated that chair. I knew he could feel my energy there but still needed to ask if I was in the chair, and I would say, "Yes, honey, I am still in the chair."

Eventually over time, I made it all the way back into my bed, and even then, there would be nights where he would call for me. He would sound a bit like Stewie Griffin from *Family Guy:* "Mom! Mom! Mom!" If you do not know what I am talking about, when you get a chance, look it up, as it is funny.

I would try to get up before he woke anyone else up, which was pretty much instantly. I would ask him if he was okay. Did he need anything? He would respond with either two or three things. One would be that he needed a glass of water, or two he would say "I love you." Or that he needed a hug. This, of course, all happened at one or two in the morning. The water was literally three feet away. In addition, couldn't he share the sweet comment in normal waking hours? My very next thought was, *I will suck it up and take it*. These moments are priceless.

Roger has always joked that he could lie gasping with his last, dying breath, and I would not budge. But if the kids let out even the littlest sneeze or sigh; I would be up in a hot flash. Waking in the middle of the night was not a big deal for me. Especially when Ryan would say, "Mom, I love you!" or "Mom, I need a hug." It just melted my heart. I will hold on to those moments forever.

How tired is tired? Tired enough that I was falling asleep at 8:00 or 8:30 at night. This did not seem to be a surprise, especially on the days I worked out at the gym. So, being tired was normal, and I thought nothing of it. It was just the way things were when one has kids, in addition to a rigorous exercise routine.

In all the books I have read and podcasts I listen to, sleep is the most important thing I can do for my health. Sleep equates to good health. That's all there is to it. Did the lack of sleep equate to my ovarian cancer? Who knows? I don't, and I am sure I will never know. I am okay with that. That is not the point. I know that when people get quality sleep, their brain can recharge. Without eight hours of adequate sleep, the body is not able to do this. It helps build immunity for your body to fight illness. When we are asleep, our body can produce an immune response. When we receive eight hours of quality sleep, our health is stronger.

I didn't really sleep through the night for over a decade, which may have weakened my immune system. If it was down, maybe my body couldn't fight the cancer that was growing. Like I said before, I will never know. It is just something that keeps the monkey brain going when I get into the why of it. Going down that rabbit hole leads to a never-ending abyss of more questions and needless worry. I choose not to go there. I have always geared my questions towards "What's next?" Not "Why?" As that truly is a never-ending cycle of needless stress.

The more I read, the more I researched, the more I realized no one is healthy. We live in a world of toxicity. This comes in more ways than I care to count. I thought I was doing all the right things. I may have been, but for my body maybe not enough. I am more aware now. More in tune with what I must do. No, scratch that, what I need to do. The necessity right now is to live a life disease free. More than anything else in this entire world, that is my focus. I have a vision that I will be like one of those centurions who live in the blue zones. Ultimately, more than any other health tip I have learned, getting quality sleep is essential for a long and healthy life!

INCONTINENCE

Getting older has its trials. There are some issues that just come along with the gig—incontinence being one. It is so incredibly inconvenient! Having to know where all the bathrooms are. Not being able to jump on a trampoline with my kids. That one is okay because I dislike being jostled around. So, that one goes in the plus category. Not to mention, that no matter where I go, I need to make sure I have enough pantyliners. Having incontinence was the first actual sign I noticed, telling me I felt a bit off. *This is just something that happens when you get older, right?* I did not think too much about it. Several friends in my peer group, some older, some my age, seemed to be experiencing similar symptoms. It all seemed legit.

This is where I should have listened to my intuition. I remember thinking . . . *Humm I am only forty-one. That is kind of early for all this incontinence business, isn't it? In my case, yes!* I was told, by my doctor that sometimes as one gets older, muscles within our core move around. They get weaker. This, of course, happens if we don't pay attention to them. Every woman has this amazing chi, and strength in our pelvic area. We just forget about it! It is like a long-lost college girlfriend we lost touch with ten years down the road. At the inevitable reunion, we reconnect, and well, you can imagine! Party Time!

Through yoga, I've developed an understanding about my core strength, and how important it is. I practice yoga, but I am still a novice and knew I needed more help. I went to see a pelvic specialist. She suggested I get Ben Wa balls. Ben what? Yes, I can't believe I am sharing this, but I am. They are also known as vagina balls. Yup, they are a real thing. I had never heard of them and was truly embarrassed, but I decided to give them a go—supposedly to help my vaginal and pelvic floor muscles: to wake them up and activate them again. I put these in. They felt weird. But I thought: If I do this, all my problems will be solved. If these Ben Wa balls can help with my incontinence, it's worth it. I am not sure they did too much, but they were an interesting conversation starter.

A year later, I was still having issues. My gym had a ladies' night. We would work out for about a half hour and socialize afterwards. This night we had a special guest, a pelvic-incontinence specialist. About twenty women filled the gym. We were all sitting, listening intently, hanging on her every word as she told us that the way we lift heavy weights can create issues. Basically, holding our breath while lifting or doing certain exercises stains our muscles in the pelvic area.

When women work out, breathe. Do not hold your breath. That made sense. I might have been holding my breath when I should have been breathing. *I can fix that—, no problem.*

I was so desperate to get help with my incontinence that I made an appointment to see what else she could do to help me. She gave me some advice. She said to be a "just in case" bathroom person. . .For example, getting ready to go somewhere, go to the bathroom beforehand. Hence, "just in case." I did this for a month, and the incontinence improved. It relieved me, as it really was a pain in the butt. She also handed me pee pills. I was having mucus discharge—almost like with a yeast infection. I thought it was just normal. She said, "Take these pills." If the discharge was the color of the pill, all was good, it was an incontinence problem. If not, then something else was going on.

So what did I do . . .? I never took the pills. Looking back now, I see that had I taken them, it might have gotten me into the doctor a couple of years sooner! But hey, who the heck knows? This is where I was at that stage of the game. That is why I am sharing all this with you.

Look further and listen to your body! Maybe I took the easy way out. All these symptoms seemed to be understandable, nonlife threatening. They made sense. Lots of women have incontinence. I just thought I was joining the club. I also thought that because I had both my kids naturally, without pain meds, things in my body were not the same as pre-kids. As I look back, maybe I subconsciously avoided realizing what was really going on. The fear of the unknown, and what it might be. I will never know! Learn from me. If you are experiencing anything like this . . . go get checked!

PAIN IN ABDOMEN

At first, it was just a twinge every now and again. At times, a quick sharp pain like someone was in there, stabbing me with a knife. One thought, which I entertained for a while, was that maybe I strained a muscle in a workout. Another thought was: *I might be in early menopause*. This made sense, as when I was a teenager, my mom told me she was not feeling right . . . periods changing, mood swings, hot flashes, so on and so forth. I told her I thought she was going through menopause. It was a bit of a surprise because she looked and acted too young for all that.

In my case, I assumed the abdomen pain was just menstrual cramps. I had always had bad cramps until my kids. Then they were not as bad. So, my periods were changing now, I concluded, bringing the bad cramps back.

A relationship-survival tidbit

My wonderful husband had a data spreadsheet when my periods would arrive. He tracked them, noting when I started and ended. The moment I began getting a little "sensitive," we knew, oh yes, "Aunt Flow" is coming to town. You may think that it was kind of crass. I mean, who does this? It was genius, as we do not fight really at all, and I feel that having this chart in place is one reason. I for one truly appreciated it, as it helped me be more mindful of my moods and feelings. I told him I was writing this in the book. He said he made the spreadsheet for himself, as a reminder. Basically, we all had to be a bit more aware at a certain time each month!

Towards the end of the summer, we were visiting dear friends of ours. Their first two kids are about the same age as ours. They had three kids, with a fourth on the way. We were up talking one night into the late hours. We started the conversation about how I too might be pregnant. It was not something that we were sharing, but they are like family. A couple of days later, Roger came home with a pregnancy test. I guess he wanted to know, since my periods were a bit off. We know this because of his awesome period spreadsheet.

The data was just not adding up. Time to find out.

Trying to wrap my brain around adding a third kid, I open the brown paper bag, pull out the box, and take the test. Just the thought of another kiddo had me rearranging the house, wondering where child number three would go. *Do we bunk the kids up or turn the loft into another bedroom? Okay, one step at a time.* I was getting way ahead of myself.

In the past, we had always looked at the test together. Once, I was too excited and—not intending to—looked seconds before he did. This time we both look at the stick at the same time. The test. Negative.

It was almost like the earth stopped moving. I did not know what to think. I felt relief and sadness all at the same time. Having another little one in our family would make things a bit more interesting. But two kids—and not being outnumbered—has always been our plan.

After I processed this information, it hit me. *If I am not pregnant, then what in the world could be going on?* This was another one of those signs I should have paid closer attention to. Not being pregnant meant something else was in the works. But what? And how serious?

This boomeranged back to my doctor, Dr. Jackie Fields, who had mentioned that menopause can be a slow process. It often creeps up over ten years to get to the actual beginning stages. Add the fact that my mom went through early menopause, and that my periods were changing. All these signs and symptoms made logical sense. This was in a cycle of how the body works; there was nothing to worry about.

Having a partner in life that I trust and can truly be myself with is such a gift. He loves me for me, and all that comes with it! That, among many other reasons, is why I married him. He knows me very well. So well, in fact, that he knew I needed a little nudge to call the doctor, as I often try to pretend things away. Especially when I know the outcome is not how I want it to be.

I remember when we got married, he asked me what I needed from him, and I said, "I'll need help every now and again to not let me hide in the clouds. Basically, I need you to hold me accountable," I said. I am so very blessed that God put him in my life. He is my rock!

As mentioned, there was one symptom sure to get me to the doctor: pain during sex. Yup, the S in B.A.S.I.I.S. saved my life.

Every couple of months, I was experiencing pain during sex. Not sure when it started. At first, it was every now and again. Then every couple of months. Then it progressed, getting more and more severe every time. Roger said it was now really concerning, I should go see Dr. Fields at the first available appointment date, Roger was right. No longer could I ignore the severity of the situation.

Under the circumstances, calling a doctor was, of course, not a hard thing for him to convince me to do. It was early September. I switched appointments with my daughter, who had a routine visit scheduled with Dr. Fields in just a couple of weeks. This was the best of all options, as our family doctor books out months in advance.

I even remember the phone call. As I talked to the receptionist, Christine, she asked the purpose of the appointment. I said, "There is this pain in my abdomen. It may be something, but I do strength training, so maybe I pulled a muscle; it might be workout related. Maybe I repeatedly injured it, but I want to be sure." There is one thing we knew it wasn't. We knew we were not pregnant. That box was checked.

I remember trying to talk myself into thinking I was still fine: that why should I take my 11-year-old daughter's appointment? If you are a mom, I am sure you understand. Being a mom is putting our kids first. That is just what we do. Considering it was her wellness appointment and she was well, however, it was okay to switch. I also knew that this was one of those *put the oxygen mask on yourself first, then your kids* type moments. If I kept my December appointment, I would have days and days of time. Time that I did not need to think about what "it" could be. I really did not ever think it could be anything serious, and "cancer!" Never once did it cross my mind!

In the grand scheme of things, what difference does a couple months make? I mean, really, just a couple of months. In my case, the difference would have been devastating! I did not know what a life-threatening situation I was in. I know without a doubt that it would have been one crazy train trip for sure. I would have been running to catch the next one. That was not going to happen. Not if I could help it! The next train that would arrive would inevitably be stage IV. Thinking about it makes the hairs on my arms stand up on end. Honestly, I can't even let my mind go there!

I am so forever grateful to have been able to have caught this when we did. I say this with all certainly. Time is everything! Catch the early train! You have the power to take over. Oversee your health! Even if you think it is nothing, go see a doctor anyway! Take it from me, it is better to know.

---

1. "What Every Woman Should Be Aware of about Ovarian Cancer," Northwest Community Healthcare, September 17, 2020, https://www.nch.org/news/what-every-woman-should-be-aware-of-about-ovarian-cancer/.

Chapter 7

Myth # 2

How could I have Cancer? . . . I'm an Athlete

> Remember, all things are possible for those who believe. — Gail Devers

I would not have always called myself an athlete. I can tell you, though, I have been active my whole life! Growing up in Canada, I did figure skating and cross-country skiing. As I got older, my sport of choice was softball. My dad throwing countless fly balls in the backyard, good memories. He helped me not fear the ball. *Just get under it!* In my junior-high years, I was on the swim team. I also dabbled in golf, yoga, roller blading, etc. Basically, I would give anything a go. Even kickboxing at-home Tae Bo workouts with Billy Blanks. As long as I can remember, I've engaged in activities, given anything a go, even if it's double time (doing the exercise twice as fast as the normal speed, in my living room).

About seven years ago, I really started to utilize this amazing backyard we call "Colorado." Live in these parts long enough, and it will eventually get to you too. My husband got me interested in running. I was never really a fan. I was one of those people who would only run if someone was chasing me. Okay, that is not altogether true. In middle school, I ran track. We competed in a long-distance event, me and two other teammates. After a bit I looked around. To my amazement, I noticed I was the only one left running from my team. Everyone else bowed out. For one, I did not know you could do that. Anyway, it is not in my nature. Never occurred to me that if I got tired, I could just pack it in. Somewhere in me, I had to keep going, no matter how hard it was. Even though I did not like running, I could not let my school down. Not sure if we won or not. It was a memory of a life lesson I never forgot: *Do not give up, no matter how hard things get.*

Almost every day, Roger went running four to five miles. One day I went with him. I just did not want to slow him down. Eventually, it became a routine we enjoyed together. The more I ran, the more I noticed the therapeutic effects that came with it. One perk was that I could eat anything I wanted. I run; therefore, I eat! That theory did not last too long, but it was fun while it lasted. There is a saying: "Staying fit lies in nutrition. Exercise is 20 percent, and nutrition is 80 percent."

Living in a palace that just begs to be played in is such a treasure! There are countless people from all over the world who come here for adventure. Thinking of running endurance races started seeping into my head. Half marathons, to be exact. It was one of those goals that were there, but I never really was too serious about it. One reason was, the distance alone was intimidating, 13.1 miles. This fictitious goal was one I could fantasize about but not really take any action steps to achieve. This was back in 2013. Then my crazy thoughts seeped out into the world. I heard once that those thoughts are prayers. There you have it: my endurance-running-goal prayers were answered. This next story is exactly how it all played out.

I was having breakfast with some friends, one morning. The summer running season of 2013 was upon us. The breakfast table buzzed with animated conversations of past races. It sounded like so much fun—the ups and downs of running and all that comes with it. What I remember feeling was the comradery of it all! Without thinking, I opened my big mouth and said that I had always wanted to run a half marathon. I couldn't really believe I said it out loud. It's like I looked around me to see who said that, and low and behold it was me!

I still wanted that thought to be mine and mine alone. That way, I didn't have to follow through. I could just talk about doing it. As in the tube of toothpaste metaphor, once the toothpaste is out, it's impossible to put it back. When I say I am going to do something I am going to do it, no turning back. This is how I hold myself accountable in my life.

Not a skip of a beat later, my friend James jumped on it. He said the Heart & Sole Half Marathon would take place in a couple months. I could join him. I looked up, totally bewildered, as I couldn't believe what he just said. James drew the line in the sand, and I crossed it. No excuses. So, bam! Just like that, I signed up.

Considering this was my first half marathon, my goal was to just finish. I felt like I was doing well. Then right before I was at the Mile 10 water station, I started fading. I thought: *Oh, man, this is what wall runners always talk about, the wall, and I have hit it.* I looked over and in the distance. I saw the finish line. I saw it. Immediately, I told myself: *I think I can make it.* As I was talking myself into that concept, I looked again. The finish line appeared further away. It was like I had another 13 miles to go instead of 3.1.

For a moment I thought it was because I was a newbie—that I was being played. They had me sign up for a full marathon, not a half. *Okay, very funny guys, ha-ha! So, here I am at the Mile 10 water station,* I thought to myself. *Hey, if this is where it ends, then this is where it ends. Half the challenge is just getting out there and giving it a go. The growth lies in the journey.*

After this huge debate with myself, I just put one foot in front of the other. I was in the last stretch. Then, out of nowhere, I started passing people. I couldn't believe it. What in the world was happening? *I was ready to toss in the towel at Mile 10, and now I'm passing people.*

That moment is when I caught the running bug! I can remember the feeling to this day. I had read about this happening to runners, and here it was happening to me. In my first race. Not at all a coincidence! It is another one of those God-moment things I get from time to time. God Shots, my friend calls it.

Sunrise the morning of the Heart and Soul Run August 25, 2013

As I have stated, Colorado has one of the most amazing backyards. Another epic life altering steppingstone adventure was climbing my first 14teener, in 2017. Just a couple years before my diagnosis. This adventure was pretty much inevitable. I look out our window and see these jagged formations every day. It was bound to happen one way or another. I have often heard people ask why on earth would someone climb a 14,000-foot mountain, and the response is usually, "Because it's there!"

Climbing a 14teener was not my idea. A fourteener, or "14teener," as the locals sometimes call it, is a mountain peak greater than 14,000 feet. There are fifty-eight such peaks in Colorado. Some friends of mine climb a 14teener annually. They call it Peaks for Freaks. That should have been my first sign to walk away. The climb for July 2017 was Mt. Bierstadt, elevation 14,065 feet. Not only did I make a commitment to climb, but I also talked my parents into it. It was a time I will forever hold in my heart!

We woke up super early to hit the trail. My dad knew we needed to get out there early, so we did. My mom brought enough Trail Mix for the entire mountain. That is just her—she always comes prepared. After starting off together, we separated, as my dad kept saying, "Run your own race." That translates into "Climb your own mountain." My friend Jennifer and I got to the top and took pictures, had a snack. I thought my parents should be here by now.

I started back down to see where they were. As soon as I passed an enormous boulder, I saw them both climbing up. I was so elated, as my heart was about to burst through my chest with pride! Especially since my mom was not going to summit. And then she changed her mind. When we parted ways, the clouds started to come in. She found a nice dry rock to sit on 400 feet from the summit. She told my dad, "I think I will just wait for you here . . . you go ahead." My dad responded, "We're almost there . . . you came all this way, don't quit now." My mom said, "Oh alright, let's go." I was so excited for them as this was not any normal 400 feet. You had to climb over huge boulders. The feeling of them summiting felt even better than when I made it to the top. They were rock stars on that hill! Everyone made a comment of how amazing they were, getting out there and doing it! I was having so much fun watching them on their journey. It was an absolute joy to see everyone challenge themselves. The climb was an epic adventure! It was not that we climbed a 14teener; it was the journey. A moment I will forever hold dear in my heart!

Mt. Bierstadt 07/12/17 My mom, dad— "Rock Stars"—and me

The fourteener was just one of the many events I participated in over the next four years. They ranged from ½ marathons, to marathons, to triathlons. Even then after all this, I did not consider myself an athlete. Not yet! A runner yes, a marathoner, yes, but not an athlete. Not until I started kicking things up a notch when I joined Manic Training.

In 2017, I joined Manic Training, a gym like no other, founded right in Fort Collins by a dear friend. His mission is to build a culture and environment that creates strong bodies, minds, friendships, and community. I wanted to support his new enterprise.

My husband and I already belonged to a gym we were happy with. The thought of changing was difficult. At first. For one, the word *manic* . . . was kind of intimidating. Not sure I could live up to it. In addition, my current gym had so many amenities—childcare, a huge variety of classes, a wealth of equipment, and a pool. Amenities I was not really using—except the pool. That was a nice perk! It was like being a member at a country club. I thought it was what we wanted, but as it turns out, my kids hated the childcare. Every time I attended a class, I felt like I truly did not belong there. Also, summer was ending, so the pool would close soon. I decided to give Manic a chance.

Manic Trainings motto is "Ready for Life!" Commit to three hours a week, and it will help you with anything life throws at you. The members were so welcoming. Name it. Manic helped with it. One day after class I asked Craig Gundlach, owner and founder at Fort Collins, about the acronym TRAIN RIGHT on the wall. He said:

"I created this acronym before I opened Manic because I wanted to have a clear statement of the core values that are the driving force for the community I want to build."

TRAIN RIGHT

T - Teamwork
R - Respect
A - Accountability
I - Integrity
N - Niceness

R – Realism
I- Investment
G- Gratitude
H- Humility
T- Timeliness

Training right in the Manic will help with anything outside the gym. Hence, the promise: "Ready for Life." No matter what you start, wherever you start, then grow from there. I felt confident, as I thought I was in shape. Oh, no! This is where I learned a brief lesson in humility.

My first day of Manic fell on a Monday in the fall of 2017. The very next day I called Craig and said, "I can't walk. I can't even sit down to go to the bathroom. Everything hurts! I do not think I can come in tomorrow." There was a brief pause . . . and here I was expecting him to say, "Oh, poor you, take the day off tomorrow and come in when you feel less sore."

Oh no . . . that is not what he said. Do you know what he said? He said matter-of-factly, "See you tomorrow." Gasp. What?!?! It was like I was a little kid again and replied in the same tone. "Okay, see you tomorrow." I hung up the phone, and I think I even looked at it in disbelief. What in the heck just happened?

I remember thinking: *How in hell will I be able to work out tomorrow when I can't even sit down to go to the bathroom!* I am so grateful I kept my word. I told him I would come in and I did. After workout Day Number Two, I did not look back. That is just how I roll. I listen to others, as sometimes they know me better. This is also a sign of a magnificent coach! Even better, a good friend! He encouraged me not to give up. No excuses! Here, I thought I was in great shape. Not so much! I couldn't even do one pushup. Not one! I had a lot of work to do.

This is by far the best place to be to get or stay fit. Much more than a gym, it is a place of transformation, and not just physically. The magic at Manic lies with the tribe. The Manic Tribe are the members, coaches, and families. They are the foundation of what Manic is. The owner at Fort Collins, Craig, is why the community who works out there is so strong. He talks and walks the walk. The same is true of all the coaches. No matter who is leading, it is an intense workout. In a good way! Craig is an inspiration. He guides us as we tread the waters of uncertainty. He will know before we do what we can and cannot do!

It is quite incredible to walk into a gym with such support and love! Our contribution to each other reaches far beyond the gym doors! They help me face challenges I would never think possible. This is where I get to see people transform before my very eyes. Not only in the obvious physical changes, but mentally and spiritually as well. To change and get the support to be *your best you* is fabulously inspirational! Little did I know when I started Manic that it would be essential to my fight with cancer.

It was after being a member a little over a year that I got diagnosed. I was getting my ass kicked in the intense, rigorous workouts three times a week, enjoying every minute! Not sure exactly when it happened, but during this year was the first time I truly felt like an athlete. I was getting stronger—could do a push-up! Four people I worked out with, I called the "Dream Team." I was always right on their tails. Then they would just take off, leaving me in the dust. I wanted to be as fast and as strong as the "Dream Team." I was so focused on that comparison I forgot how much I had grown! I talked with Roger about how much better than me the Dream Team were, as it concerned me.

There are two types of athletes: sprinters and endurance. We concluded maybe I am more an endurance athlete. That rang true, as marathons and triathlons are endurance sports.

It has been fun, working out with Roger, and the manic tribe that we bonded with every morning at 6:15. We had a standing date three times a week for over a year. To work out with him has made us not only stronger physically, but also in our relationship.

I also did an obstacle race—one of many events the Manic Tribe signed up for as a team. It was the most intense race I had ever been in. This type of obstacle, you would see on an army base: carrying sandbags, rolling a big tractor tire across the beach, carrying a huge bucket of water, carrying a heavy bowling ball up a hill. Crazy stuff! The obstacles I was most worried about were the walls. Oh yes! We had to get our whole body over two walls—one eight feet tall, the other ten. The eight-foot one was hard, but doable. The ten-foot one just about ate my lunch.

I got some advice before the race on how to best go about getting over these walls. The strategy was to go for it and not stop, just give it your all. The obstacle race rules were, if you had to have help to get over the wall you got disqualified. I would not let that happen. I was holding my own, keeping up, feeling good! Then I saw the walls.

At the first one, I thought to myself: *I got this*. It was my turn to go over. I ran and gave it my all. Up and over. Whew! The ten-foot wall was next. There actually was a wee step to help. It gave me the assistance I very much needed. Here I go . . . wall number two. My turn is up. I ran. I used the little step. I'm up . . . I am up; I am up. And I can't get over it. I'm stuck.

I was like a monkey stuck in a tree. A very uncoordinated monkey stuck in a tree. I look behind me. Uh-oh, there is a line forming. Maybe if I just moved my body this way and that way, I could get over it. Everyone was cheering me on. I would not give up. No matter what, I was going to get over that wall. I felt like I had to let some people go ahead. I did not know this, but you can take as many chances as you need to. After someone told me that, I came down and let all the waiting people go past. A kind soul asked if I wanted a boost. Politely, I said, "No, thank you; I got this." He said, okay, then told me to put my outer leg over first. Oh, man, that's what I was doing wrong. I did not know that I had put my inner leg over, and that was why it was so hard.

At this point, my arms are shot! That does not matter. This wall was not going to win. If this takes me all day, I am going to get over it.

Finally, I got my second wind and put myself back in the game. I started running. This time, I made it over. I got over it! Holy moly, I got over the wall! I started crying, as that is what I do. As I was running to the next obstacle I was still crying, I couldn't stop. It was the hardest thing I had ever done in my life! I couldn't believe it. I look up. I see Roger, as he has finished his wave and come back to run the rest of the race with me. It was so exciting to see him. I started to tell him what happened. Somehow, I completely forgot I was still in the race. He snapped me out of it, saying, "Go, go, go, you're in a race!" Oh, yeah. With grit and determination, I finished! I did not complete two of the obstacles.

That did not matter. I had a blast. I accomplished something I thought I could never do!

Here is the icing on the cake. As I was going over the walls, the event photographer just happened to be there. Here I am on my first attempt to get over. I giggle every time I see them. I also remember how incredible it felt to achieve what I thought was the most impossible task in the world. Being involved in this race with my Manic Tribe was just one of those God coincidences. This was in his plan, as he knew what challenges lay ahead, and how much this would help to get me through. As they say, a picture is worth a thousand words.

Cerus Fitness Race 10/07/2018

I mean, really!?! My legs look like they are not even attached to my body! Sometimes challenges are not so pretty and finding comic relief is essential!

The next year on July 27, 2019, I ran "The Human Race" ½ marathon. This was an annual event that the members of manic participated in as a team. The event has a variety of lengths to run: 5K (3.1 miles), 10K, (6.2 miles) and a ½ marathon (13.1 miles). Roger and I decided to do the half marathon. There was not too much that I remember in this race except I ran it side by side with Roger. We encouraged each other along the way and had fun. As we finished, family, friends, and our kids met us at the finish. Little did I know this was going to be the last race I would be running for a while. It was only two months later that I found out I had stage 3C ovarian cancer.

Human Race July 27, 2019 Two months before my diagnosis

In the following months, every time I thought I could not go another step, I kept going. Every time I was sure I had to turn in the towel, raise the white flag, the excuses dissipated. I found grit and determination instead. All these past events prepared me for my cancer fight. They brought people into my life who inspired me to be a risk taker, to challenge myself. To be my best me!

Having these moments of accomplishment were in no way a coincidence. They were set in place as markers from the universe, knowing I needed to have experienced conquests of exertion to prepare me for the hardest encounter of my life! I needed these conquests of exertion in my life experience.

One challenge in particular, I remember participating in a week before my first oncologist appointment. I was at Manic. The workouts themselves are timed to the minute, and there are often "finishers" (challenges after the workout). Even with this pain in my abdomen, I still took part—somehow, I still convinced myself it was a pulled muscle, or something that would eventually go away with time. The "finisher" was to hold a plank position for five minutes. This isometric bodyweight exercise involves holding a flat back to strengthen the core. If you stopped short of the time he set, Craig would throw down a resistance band in front of you. The goal was to make it the full five minutes with no bands. Deep down, I knew I could do this. I would just have to dig deep! *There is no way I am giving up, no way!* These five minutes seemed endless! I needed to push through! If you have ever done a plank, you know five minutes is extra-long, like an eternity.

It was another sign. A feeling I felt in my gut! My intuition signaling how important it was to stay strong. To do whatever I needed to hold the plank. I tried several tactics to get me through. One, instead of thinking about the whole five minutes, I broke it up into parts. I told myself: *If I can make it to two minutes, then maybe I can take a break.* The two minuets came and went. Then I thought: *If I make it to three minutes, then I can take a break.* That time came and went, so it was in that moment that I could really accomplish this feat. Another tactic was, I closed my eyes and went to my dream place. I pictured myself on a sandy beach with bright blue skies, watching the ocean waves come in. Finally, I kept telling myself: *Do not give up*. Another thought occurred to me: *If I make it for the full five minutes, I'll be able to survive whatever is coming*—even though I had no idea what that would be. So, when things got hard, I had all these experiences to look back on for strength.

These past events were my building blocks to prepare me for the biggest event of my life! As I shared earlier, I usually enter at least one big event every year. I did not enter any events in 2020, because fighting cancer was my event. It was the biggest, hardest challenge I had ever had to face! After the very last chemo treatment, I got to ring the bell and I in time earn my one-year string of beads. More details on the beads yet to come.

It all started after the first meeting with Dr. Guntupalli. On September 13, 2019, the day of my diagnosis, he told me about an ovarian-cancer support group, Colorado Ovarian Cancer Alliance (COCA). He suggested that I look them up. That very night when it was close to midnight, and I couldn't sleep, so what did I do? I went online and looked up COCA. I was befuddled when I saw that at 9:00 the next morning, September 14, 2019, they were having their first annual COCA awareness walk, in Fort Collins. I couldn't believe the timing. At 9:00 the next morning I was going to be at that walk.

When I woke up, I asked if anyone wanted to go with me. Roger said there is no other place that we should be.

There was a sea of turquoise everywhere. We walked up to the event registration table. The man asked if I was a caregiver or a survivor. Not knowing how to answer, I said, "What do you mean?" He went on to tell me that if I went one or more years as a cancer survivor, then I could get that many necklaces. I, of course, having found out only eighteen hours earlier, said, "I found out yesterday. You would not happen to have one with one bead on it, would you?" He stared at me, then Roger, then back at me. He said, "You are a survivor. You are Day One and that is a survivor in my book." He then went on to hand me a string of bright turquoise beads. It did not feel right, as I was not one year yet. I was just one day. Even then, I still had the laparoscopy in two days to see if it was cancer. I was still banking on being in that 1 percent of it not being cancer. Well, sort of. I knew. Somehow, I just knew that Dr. Guntupalli was right in his diagnosis, but a little part of me was still hoping for a miracle.

After I got my beads for my one day as a survivor, we called the kids over. The walk was about to start. At first, I was reluctant to interact. Roger said, "We are here for a reason. Go talk to some of these women." It was out of character for him to urge me to talk to these women, as I am the one who has never met a stranger. But that morning I was not myself. I had just received news that rocked me world. I was scared. I remember feeling apprehensive about approaching anyone.

But I looked up and saw a bright neon-green shirt with the words "Team Hansen." She told me her name: Amy. She was six years in remission. I told how amazing I thought it was. She congratulated me on one year. She knew that, of course, because I was wearing one strand of beads.

Still feeling like an imposter, I came clean. I told her that I just I found out yesterday and that they gave me the string of beads anyway. Her reaction was unforgettable. With such empathy in her eyes, she immediately gave me a hug. We became instant friends. Amy shared her story, and I asked as many questions as I could on a short walk of only about three quarters of a mile. Afterwards, there was an incredible breakfast and more conversations with some fantastic women. Then a big group picture. I remember I had to hold back tears, trying to smile, as I knew that in that moment I was a part of an ovarian-cancer group. Not there to support, but intricately a part of. That is a feeling I had never experienced before.

It was quite surreal. I am so incredibly fortunate to have gone on the internet the night before, or I would never have met these remarkable people, who supported me every step in my journey then and now. When we got home, I took the necklace off. It sat on my closet shelf for a year. I told myself that when I hit a year, I would hang it up with my other medals. As you have read, I have had some tough challenges, but nothing like fighting for my life. I am so excited to tell you that a year later it was one of the most gratifying moments to hang up the beads I got on that iconic fall day. This was another universal timing gem. I had my past events to help me stay in the game—one step, one day, one treatment at time!

Ovarian Cancer Survivor Necklace on the far right.

I did it then. I can do it now! This is not going to get me!

Chapter 8

Myth # 3

How could I have Cancer? . . . It's not in My Family

To get any knowledge about our ancestry is a gift. —
Sean Hays

"Family history is the biggest risk factor for ovarian cancer," says Dr. Chi. "However, people with a family history of the disease make up only 10 to 15 percent of those diagnosed."[1]

Ovarian cancer is not in my family. That was one of my first thoughts after my diagnosis. I was perplexed. No one on either side of my family had had it. If it ran in my family, then for sure I'd have been on the lookout. Probably have recognized the signs earlier. That was not the case. I had always thought that cancer was gene related. How in the world did I have it and why?

Roger and I wanted to know more. We thought having more information would clarify the complexity of the relationship between family genes and cancer. This led us to see a genetic counselor. A medical professional who would help us evaluate the risk factors for hereditary cancer. Our gene counselor helped us understand how the genes work vis-à-vis cancer. She described it in a way that made sense to me: *Just because you get an invitation to the ball does not mean you go.*

The National Institute of Health National Cancer Institute adds the following explanations:

> If a cancer-susceptibility variant is present in a family, it does not necessarily mean that everyone who inherits the variant will develop cancer. Several factors influence whether a given person with the variant will actually develop cancer. One is the penetrance of the variant. When not all people who carry a variant go on to develop the disease associated with that variant, it is said to have incomplete or reduced penetrance. Hereditary cancer syndromes can also vary in their expressivity—that is, people who inherit the variant may vary in the extent to which they show signs and symptoms of the syndrome, including the development of associated cancers. Lifestyle factors and environmental risks can also influence disease expression. [2]

That is, just because you have a cancer gene does not mean you will develop cancer. The reasoning is that if the gene runs in the family, the chances increase. That just means a predisposition based in the cancer gene. It can be dormant—until something else wonky wakes it up, and then it takes over. After the blood work and additional consultation, the National Institute of Health National Cancer Institute website goes on, "in the case of a negative test result, it is important that the person's doctors and genetic counselors ensure that that person is receiving appropriate cancer screening based on that person's personal and family history and any other risk factors they may have. Even when the genetic testing is negative, some individuals may still benefit from increased cancer surveillance."

It turned out I did *not* have a predisposition to ovarian cancer! As a matter of fact, they tested close to twenty other cancers that I might have the genetic makeup for. They, along with the ovarian-cancer gene test, came back negative. This was a relief on a variety of levels.

One, the likelihood of my daughter Kela getting ovarian cancer from my genes is very low. In addition, my cousins and other family members can rest a little easier, as I do not have the predisposition for ovarian cancer. That does not mean we will not be on the lookout, as cancer can show up in many ways. It just means that I am not a carrier of a recessive genetic condition. I do not have a dormant cancer gene that may or may not come to life one day. This is where the study of epigenetics can help. According to the Centers for Disease Control and Prevention (CDC), genes play an important role in your health, but so do your behaviors and environment, such as what you eat and how physically active you are. Epigenetics is the study of how your behaviors and environment can cause changes that affect the way your genes work. Unlike genetic changes, epigenetic changes are reversible and do not change your DNA sequence, but they can change how your body reads a DNA sequence.

Gene expression refers to how often or when proteins are created from the instructions within your genes. While genetic changes can alter which protein is made, epigenetic changes affect gene expression to turn genes "on" and "off." Since your environment and behaviors, such as diet and exercise, can result in epigenetic changes, it is easy to see the connection between your genes and your behaviors and environment. [3]

My dear friend Beth got an invitation to the ball. She tested positive for the BRACA2 gene. In addition, she has a family history of breast and ovarian cancer. Because she was done having kids, she decided to have the full hysterectomy. In addition, ovarian cancer is hard to screen for, and her risk was so high she did not want to gamble. It is a risk no one should have to face. Now, remember, *just because she has the gene does not mean it will turn into cancer*. The news of having the gene is hard enough. Then to top it all off, not knowing if or when it will develop. Unbearable! This is one ball no one wants an invitation to, much less to go to the actual ball. Honestly, there is not a good way to know. The only way to be proactive is to have biannual exams, for like forever. Beth was forty-one when she decided to take a very proactive approach: a full hysterectomy. Her courage was so palpable. Maybe if I had been more on top of it, I would not have developed cancer. Yet, it didn't enter my realm of awareness, as it was not in my family. Moreover, there is so much information out there. It is like a unique puzzle that only pertains to you. A huge advantage is to know your family history and how genetics and epigenetics can influence your health. These are only small pieces of your puzzle. For your own peace of mind, and curiosity, it would behoove you to conduct your own research to gather more pieces for your puzzle. That way, you get a complete picture and know what you are dealing with.

Growing up, I heard a story about my maternal grandma. In her sixties she had a cyst that grew into a grapefruit-sized tumor. Fortunately, it was benign. The moment we found out that I had a tumor, it was like I was in a time warp. Bouncing from doctor to ultrasound to a CT, then back to the doctor, all within a week, was a lot to take. I tried to convince myself that whatever was there, don't worry. *It will be just like Grandma Bunny. She had a tumor, and it was benign.* I truly thought the same scenario was going to be me. That, of course, was not the case. Not by a long shot!

Family history is important. Several years before my diagnosis—during an annual wellness visit—Dr. Fields told me, "The daughter's menstrual cycle and age of menopause usually follows in the same path as her mother's." My grandma, my mom, and I had difficult periods. My mom told me how at my grandma's first period, she thought she was bleeding to death. Her mother did not talk about this kind of thing. Oh, how my heart felt for her. I think that is why my mom and I have always been so open with one another. For example, when I was five, my mom had the "birds and bees" talk. Many topics can be embarrassing, but not for me and my mom. We share everything. It shocks my Roger every time when we share girly things. This tradition of openness, I have carried on with my kids.

In Chapter 6, I mentioned that when my mom was in her mid-forties, she was experiencing symptoms of early menopause and not aware of it. As the old saying goes, "If you are in it, you can't see it." She transitioned through menopause without any therapy or traditional hormone replacement drugs. I remember her using a bit of progesterone to help with some symptoms. It seemed to do the trick, as she managed without any complications and did not feel the need for anything else. About a decade later, at the age of fifty-seven, my mom began experiencing extreme pain in her abdomen. Her doctor ordered a CA-125 test. The count turned out to be high, but the number was not revealed to her. It was monitored for a month with no improvement. She was still experiencing pain, with a rising CA-125.

After a consultation with her doctor, my mom made the brave decision to have a full hysterectomy. After surgery the doctor informed my mom that she had benign cysts on her ovaries. He also went on to share that before surgery he was confident, he was going to find cancer. Fortunately, that was not the case!

Hmm, this sounds oddly familiar. I remember thinking: *How in the world is this my life right now? This has to be a dream! I'm living someone else's life, or who knows, maybe I am living a past life.*

Nothing made sense. I mentally tried to draw a straight line as to why I had cancer. If I could draw a line from A to B, then maybe I could make more sense of all this. On the other hand, even were I able to draw a line as to why or how this happened, it did not change the fact. It happened. It is what it is! The only thing I could do was to look forward. I started reading and gathering all the info I could. The more information I gathered, the more complex and confused I became. One component that was not so complex but was essential for daily survival was my positive attitude, which has always been my superpower.

Every doctor I saw asked me about my family's history. Cancer has been a part of my family history, but not ovarian. It is truly shocking, and heart wrenching that cancer is so prevalent in our world. The heartache, anguish, and pain it has caused is unfathomable.

About a decade ago, we lost a very dear friend. He battled lung cancer. He never smoked, not ever. It was shocking because I thought that lung cancer and smoking went hand in hand. How could this happen? He was a young father of two, happily married to an incredible woman, and an incredible human being. But cancer does not care that you have a family, how old you are, or that you are a good person. It was so tragic. Trying to ask why got me nowhere.

Just recently, our neighbor's son passed away from this awful disease. Ben was eleven, such a special soul. His humor, tenacity, and kindness were infectious! He was full of life, with a genuine passion to help others. He fought the big fight every day. Sadly, his little body just wore out. His spirit lives on in all of us who were blessed to know him.

We got to know Ben and his parents, as I went through treatments at the same time. After one of my transfusions, I was exhausted, and not really feeling good. But I went to visit him. Amy, Ben's mom, said I didn't need to come, but I wanted to. I wanted to do this for Ben. To give him a package. The family spent so much time at the hospital that they had rented a little apartment right next to it, so as not have to travel an hour every day for his treatments. Before my infusion, I had picked up a package filled with all kinds of goodies: cards, notes, candy, and toys. Just a few things to help Ben feel better, even temporarily. No matter how I felt, I was going to go.

Amy opened the door to their apartment, and all I remember was his beautiful smile. I immediately felt better. Here, I had wanted to help him, but what really happened is he helped me. I was so taken aback, as they had a little something for me too. The kindest family ever! Even fighting this fight, they were thinking of others. It was a blanket and slipper socks. Ben thought it would help during my infusions, as he knew all too well you get extremely cold. This is just how he was. A kind, pure heart. No matter how bad I felt, I got strength from his positive energy! He helped me tremendously, and he will always have a special place in my heart!

I know we are not on earth forever. That does not make it any easier when we lose loved ones. A friend helped me cope with the loss. He said, "God needs kind souls up in heaven too." Recently, I heard a Buddhist priest say, "The reason grief is so hard is not that we loved them, but that they loved us." So meaningful and true. As humans, we do not know when our time is up, or why we go, or how. What matters is what we do here on earth, and not to waste a single minute. Life is so precious and instead of asking why, I turn that question over to my higher power. I am blessed to be able to continue to live my best life possible, filled with gratitude, kindness, and love. In memory of those I have lost. I hold them all in my heart and look up at the stars, and know they are angels that watch over me.

From Christmas celebrations, to anniversaries, to even basic card games, many of my best childhood memories involve my grandparents. Oh, how my family loves games. That was one constant, growing up. We always played games. I feel very privileged to have been born into such a loving family! We may not see one another often, but that does not mean we would not do or be there in an instant for one another!

As I was growing up, my grandparents and cousins lived at a distance, but when we visited, time was eternal. Even now, I can close my eyes and I am right back in time, as we have always kept the stories alive so that even when we lost someone, that person was always alive in our hearts.

The medical history of my grandparents is as follows. My maternal grandparents had cancer. My grandma was a breast-cancer survivor. She had a partial radical mastectomy. In addition, in advanced age at age eighty-seven she had ministrokes, which caused some brain damage. The result was, she developed dementia. She never lost her jovial spirit and lived to be ninety-four. My grandfather had asthma as a kid but worked in car dealerships and places with very poor ventilation as an adult and developed emphysema. At seventy-five, he died from lung cancer. My grandpa on my paternal side died of stomach cancer. He was eighty-four. My grandma Betty lived to be one hundred and two, in good health, with all her faculties. Even though each of them but my grandma Betty had cancer, it was at the end of a full life. Which still did not make it easy when they passed. My grandparents are a part of me, and I know they watch over me and our family every day!

Good news! The gene specialist told me that the likelihood of me passing ovarian cancer down to Kela, my daughter, is very low. It was a huge concern, but that does not mean we are not going to be mindful in the future. Not only that, but the chances that my cousins and their kids are at risk is very low. This was the best news ever. This cancer that grew in me was not gene related. That is one of the many reasons I am so passionate about sharing this with you! Cancer can still happen, even if it does not run in the family.

Since we are in the family zone, I want to share a bit more about how my family was my rock through all of this and continues to be. Not only for the obvious reasons—like taking care of the kids, being by my bedside, basically anything I needed. They were all there! My favorite thing to do with my family is to create memories. Since we live in different parts of North America, we usually vacation together somewhere tropical. This time, right in the middle of my cancer chemo therapies in 2019, we got the chance to go to down near the Bahamas, to the coral islands of Turks and Caicos—by far, the best trip I have ever taken in my life. Some vacations are activity based, or culturally based. This one was just what the doctor ordered—peaceful, rejuvenating, and very relaxing.

The trip was on the calendar well before my diagnosis, November 30 to December 7, 2019. I asked Dr. Guntupalli if I could pull it off. He told me I needed to live my life and that we would set the infusion schedule to match the trip. Woo-hoo! The only stipulation was that I had to wear a mask on the plane. Not a problem! This was before COVID, of course. Wearing a mask would be inconvenient, but totally worth it. I was confident this was the right decision, and I was good to go. It was an experience of a lifetime.

My family still had concerns that throwing my infusions off schedule would hurt my chances of recovery. I told them it would not do any such thing. Deep down, I knew this trip was exactly what I needed. Not going would have been more harmful. I knew being with my family and an opportunity to relax was the perfect therapy!

Every day on the trip, we decided as a family where we would eat dinner. Then we would tell Sasha, our personal butler (I know, crazy), where, and she took care of all the details. One night my sister-in-law Ira organized a surprised for me.

This particular day everyone was noncommittal; we would figure it out when the time came, they said. Sounded good to me. Everyone kept the secret tight, even Sasha. I know because I asked her. And she said something to throw me off the trail. Throughout the day, I was in the dark, but I figured out something was up. I did not think a lot about it, as we were having too much fun playing in the sun! Around sunset, water activities came to an end.

Unknown to me, the staff was getting dinner all set up. I remember asking what time our reservation was and how long it would take to get there. Everyone said, oh not long, not long at all. When we were all ready, we filled out the door like little ducks. We walked out onto the front porch. I immediately knew why everyone had been acting funny all day long. Emotions took over and tears started to run down my cheeks. I was so deeply moved that I could feel it in my heart! What a phenomenal setting. Two personalized servers stood over a candlelit table with a white tablecloth, real china with elaborate place settings, and light blue balloons. They had wanted the balloons to be turquoise, the color associated with ovarian cancer, but blue was all they could find. Amazingly enough, in the time it took us to dress for dinner, the staff transported the space right outside our front door into a five-star dining room—like something set up for kings and queens. To do this, they went to one of the classy restaurants on the resort property and brought the dinner there, then set everything up out in front of our villa with all the trimmings. Just like in a dream.

Then there was the food! A luxurious menu with scrumptious appetizers, lobster—my favorite—and a variety of delicious local Caribbean cuisine. All day they worked on setting it up. Not only was this trip in itself like a utopian paradise, but also Ira went out of her way to make it even more special.

The trip was magical—in one of the most beautiful places in the world. It was also a way for me to forget, for a while, that I was sick. I honestly did not feel sick on this trip. I was living life! Not fearing or fighting for it! Totally attainable, I might add. Especially with an iconic once-in-a-lifetime trip like this one. I will forever be grateful!

There could be a myriad of reasons I got cancer. Why does it occur? To try to nail down how it happened would be a huge time waster. As I have shared before, I am okay with the mystery. I really am. The most recent information I have will help me stay in remission. On the flip side, that can change in a hot minute if I do not continue to actively do the work to ensure I stay as healthy as I can.

On some level, I think in the beginning it would have helped to know how I got cancer. Cancer is quite the conundrum. The more we can share our stories, the more survivors we will have walking this earth. Everyone's history is different. Make sure you are well versed in your history. Take it from me, if ovarian cancer does not run in your family, do not rule it out. Family history and the B.A.S.I.I.C.S. will cover so much ground in preventing ovarian cancer.

---

1. Dr. Andrew J. Roth, "5 Myths about Ovarian Cancer," https://www.mskcc.org/news/5-myths-about-ovarian.
2. Genetic Testing for Inherited Cancer Susceptibility Syndromes," National Cancer Institute (NIH), https://www.cancer.gov/about-cancer/causes-prevention/genetics/genetic-testing-fact-sheet#does-someone-who-inherits-a-cancer-susceptibility-variant-always-get-cancer.
3. Centers for Disease Control and Prevention, CDC,

Chapter 9

Myth # 4

How Could I Have Cancer? . . . I live a happy and stress-free life.

> The only thing that holds true happiness is that moment when you're in it. Nothing can be controlled— Eliza Doolittle

Happy has a different meaning for different people. What does happiness mean to you? Try not to answer right away. Just take a minute and reflect. We can define happiness in so many ways. My first thought was a visual of Julie Andrews twirling on the hilltops in Austria. For me, it's in the little things. Little moments that bring joy to my world. For example, my family brings out these moments all the time. Like watching my son walk down the street with his buddies with their arms around each other. Another, when my daughter just gives me a kiss for no reason. Or when my kids hold hands just walking down the street. Even when my husband opens the door for me when we go out. One that always gets me is when my parents make each other laugh. Even the simplest thing, such as when I get a phone call or text from my big brother. With these moments, I feel my heart just gets bigger and bigger!

I am sure you came up with a vast list of your own. I could go on and on about what makes me happy. That alone will not get me to understand what true happiness really is. These are all important, but happiness goes way deeper.

I have always had the thought that kids have all the answers. They are so intuitive, so organic and genuine. This is especially true as infants. I can just tell by their eyes that they know the secrets to life. Oh yeah, they know.

As you may have figured out by now, I love books. There is a children's picture book that stands out more than most. *The Three Questions* by Jon J. Muth, based on a story by Leo Tolstoy. It is about a young boy, Nikolai, who seeks advice from an old wise turtle named Leo. The young boy is certain the wise old turtle knows the answer to his three questions. First question: When is the best time to do things? Second, who is the most important one? Finally, what is the right thing to do? I am sure you are asking yourself where and how can I find this wise old turtle. I do not want to spoil the book, but I will leave you with this thought . . . it is about living in the moment. Not thinking about the past or the future, just now.

My life is more than I could ever dream of. This is just not something I say lightly. If I planned my life, I would sell myself short. Everything in my life, I truly feel grateful for. My relationships, my experiences, and happiness came from surrendering to what is. My parents gave me a hat for Christmas that said, "It is what it is." That is just how I roll.

After my early-September 2019 visit to Dr. Fields, I was immediately referred to a specialist and by September 18 had my diagnosis. The entire year afterwards, September 2019–September

2020, Roger made sure I had the best year ever. One day he asked me, Was it the best year ever? I do not think I gave him the answer he wanted to hear. I told him no, it was not the best year ever. Do not get me wrong. It was an amazing year. Boating, biking, creating memories with my family. Not that I did not have a bang-up year. It was that I feel that way every year. I truly do. As far back as I can remember, pick out a year in my life and I will list all the joyful things that happened. Even if it was tragic, it brings me happiness because the experience is how I became the person I am today. I am truly grateful for that insight!

I do not know about you, but I enjoy listening to how people met. The way people meet one another is fascinating to me. So many things in this world could go one way or another. Life is about choices. I know that God planned for Roger and me to cross paths at just the right time. We met when we did. Any sooner, and I do not think we would be together today. The year I met Roger was incredible. It is a unique and funny story.

I was living in Dallas. He was in Fort Collins. My parents and his aunt and uncle lived in the same community in New Mexico. For six years, his aunt and uncle had tried to introduce us. Then one day, my friend Jack happened to tell me about Fort Collins. Without him, I would have never known of this little piece of heaven. Sight unseen, I decided I wanted to live there.

While visiting my parents just afterwards, I told them the news: I was moving to Fort Collins. Roger's Aunt Mary Ann enthusiastically exclaimed, "That's where Roger lives."

As I was about to head home to Dallas, Mary Ann ran out her front door, waving a piece of paper at me. She said, "Here is Roger's email address." We emailed for about three months. My parents suggested that I at least visit the town I was going to move to, and Roger was nice enough to show me around. When I came to Fort Collins on the weekend, I pulled into his driveway. I looked up and he was waiting outside his front door with his dog, Blue. When I first saw what he looked like, I mouthed, "Oh, sh**."

Now, you might think that was a bad thing. Well, that is just what Roger thought. But on the contrary. The "Oh, sh**" was a good thing. It was a good "Oh, sh**."

He reached down, patted Blue on the head, and said to his dog, "This is going to be a l-o-n-g weekend." Love has a peculiar way when it shows itself. And as they say, the rest is history.

I for one know that when Roger and I finally met, it was one of those divine-intervention type things. I know it made my parents happy. I tell my kids: before your dad, I had to kiss a lot of frogs. My mom recounted how her friends would ask her while we were dating if we were going to get married. She refused to answer, not wanting to jinx the prospect. We just celebrated fourteen years of marriage in 2021 and are stronger than ever. I do not think she jinxed anything. He is one of the good ones through and through!

My kids, Kela and Ryan, make me happy daily! I get to be their mom. See them grow up into such incredible beings—so proud of who they are! As a parent, it is one thing I hear all the time: *I just want you to be happy*. How can they be happy if I do not show them how by living it myself? Living as an example and understanding that life is not all rainbows and unicorns. That is not how it works.

I find such happiness and empowerment in doing things for me. I learned that truly expressing self-love is not selfish; it is a necessity. I need to be on my game so that I can take care of my family. I get this through my time with friends. Lunch with the girls is life changing. It's not that often that women can find other women friends who truly get each other and support one another with no endgame. Just being there for each other. Having other people in similar situations, with all the roles we play as moms, is priceless!

The motivational speaker, self-help guru Jim Rohn, said, "You are the average of the five people you spend the most time with." He talks about how research proves that relationships matter, and that we entwine our lives with the people we associate with. The people I am the closest to influence my thinking, self-esteem, and decision-making. I can honestly think of no other reason why I am happy, healthy, and to be blunt sane. It is because of my tribe! They inspire me to be a better version of myself. I could not ask for more uplifting, motivating, and supportive people in my life!

This is another thing I learned through all this and over the years. Who we choose to spend time with matters. It is okay that I am not everyone's friend. You know the saying by Ludwig Feuerbach, a German philosopher, "You are what you eat." Well, I would assume that would go with people as well: I am who I hang out with. There are people in my world who I know have made me who I am today. I want to thank the universe for putting them in my path. No way would I be where I am right now without my amazing tribe!

This lesson, I hope to pass on to my kids sooner than later. I think it is necessary to have good people in our lives, no matter the age! It truly makes a tremendous difference. I had a conversation with my daughter about sometime-friends and genuine friends. She classifies the genuine ones as sister friends. We have had many conversations about how important it is for them to speak up for themselves if someone, anyone, including me, is not being kind or respectful. It is easier said than done, as I did not start doing this until late into my adulthood. I wanted to be liked, even at the expense of me not being true to who I am. Roger came into my life about six months after I started figuring this out. He was The One, as he loved me for me, warts and all!

Most of my life, I have been a people pleaser. At times, still kind of am. Like a chameleon, I just formed into whoever they wanted me to be. It wasn't until I was an adult that I realized that is really exhausting, and how in the heck can I find myself when I am not even paying attention to the real me? It reminds me of the John Hughes movie *The Breakfast Club*—the scene where the five high school kids who have to serve detention on a Saturday, have to each write their own essay on "Who I think I am." But Claire makes the suggestion that instead of writing five papers, they have

Brian become their voice and write one group paper. Gradually throughout the movie they discover a little more about themselves and emerge from that Saturday detention a bit clearer about who they are. That is how I feel when I am learning more about myself. Brian Johnson (acted by Anthony Michael Hall) plays the nerd. So, of course, he writes the essay for all of them, by common consent.

I talk to my kids about how to better understand their feelings: the good, the bad, and everything in between. This way, they can navigate through life, having a compass of sorts to guide them in the right direction when things get difficult. They can persevere until they find the life light that brings them to true happiness. Nothing in life comes easy. It shouldn't. Finding happiness lies in the challenges. Especially in our adventures, the rubber meets the road.

I handle challenges and stress similarly. Life experiences teach me there is a way to go through ups and downs that does not induce stress. Stress on its own is a cancer, all by itself. When I know what is about to happen, then I can respond in a more homeostatic way. My oncologist, Dr. Saketh R. Guntupalli, in *Sex and Cancer*, talks about just that. The foreknowledge of what could be a stressful situation is helpful. I control how to respond. The information will in turn decrease the stressors. It helps me prepare my mind and body. I will accept what is happening, even though I cannot control it. I can choose a more positive response.

Dr. Guntupalli also wrote about Robert M. Sapolsky, Stanford University professor of neurology and neurological sciences. Sapolsky, recognized as one of the country's foremost experts on stress, wrote *Monkeyluv: And Other Essays on Our Lives as Animals*. Reading his research on stress, I knew from experience it was true. Throughout my life and in my most recent challenge with beating my cancer, this was an essential part in my recovery! I am in remission because I had a positive mindset. I also think that this strength is just in my genes. I learned it from my experiences, and especially from my family. No matter what comes our way, we can always approach it with an acceptance of the *now*, and a "what's next?" attitude. A good tool to have to be able to handle anything!

Not only do I have the best family ever, but I also came from the best family ever. My parents mean the world to me, and my older brother has always been my superhero! Secretly, I am still trying to catch up to him. That is what little sisters do: look up to their older brother and follow in their footsteps. I remember when I graduated from college, he said, "I raised you pretty well! I'm proud of you, Li'l Sis!" I was taken back with the words: "Raised me." Isn't that the parents' job?" Well, yes and no. He also took part, but differently.

My strength comes from my parents and my brother! He pushed me in ways that no one else could. My mom and dad have always been the most generous, kind people I will ever know! The memories we shared growing up and the memories now are truly priceless! My happiness is my family. How can they not be? They are my heart and my why in this world. My *why* gives me motivation, methods, and mindfulness to continue to have an optimistic perspective.

Finding true happiness requires me to find the true me. Happiness is a privilege—something I do not do, something I have. Be your most authentic self. Happiness will always follow.

> I am not who you think I am; I am not who I think I am; I am who I think you think I am. **— Thomas Cooley**

Chapter 10

Myth # 5

How could Have I Cancer? . . . I am Healthy!

> Let food be thy medicine, and let medicine be thy food — Hippocrates

Being healthy. How do you even define the word "healthy" anymore? Being healthy or not has become so complex that it is hard to know what to believe. The word is thrown around so much the meaning is lost. That led me to look it up. This is what I found in the Google dictionary:

healthy*—adjective*

- *In good health.*
  "I feel fit and healthy"
  Similarly:
- *(of a part of the body) not diseased.*
  "healthy cells"

My reaction: A person can *feel* healthy, but not *be* healthy. I needed more explanation.

With my next search topic, I was more specific:

What does it mean to be "healthy"?

I turned to a top international source: CONSTITUTION OF THE WORLD HEALTH ORGANIZATION (WHO). Below are three of its most important principles:

• Health is a state of complete physical, mental and social well-being and not merely the absence of disease or infirmity.

• The enjoyment of the highest attainable standard of health is one of the fundamental rights of every human being without distinction of race, religion, political belief, economic or social condition.

• The extension to all peoples of the benefits of medical, psychologicaland related knowledge is essential to the fullest attainment of health. [1]

The Determinants of Health

Many factors combine together to affect the health of individuals and communities. Whether the people are healthy or not is determined by their circumstances and environment. To a large extent, factors such as where we live, the state of our environment, genetics, our income an educational level, and our relationships with friends and family all have considerable impacts on health, whereas the more commonly considered factors by public health movements such as access and use of health care services also have far reaching impact. [2]

WHO's definition makes sense to me. Where does one's health

truly lie? It's not like there is really a measuring stick, as for height, or a scale, as for weight. It's subjective, "so to speak." I "thought" I was healthy. How could I have had stage 3C ovarian cancer?

When friends started learning about my diagnosis, they would say, "How in the world do you have cancer? You're one of the healthiest people I know." I've been trying to figure this out for a couple of years myself. I will be straight with you. It is a conundrum. For one, it depends on who you talk to or what you read! There is so much information out there. It is truly so complex. For instance, eat this, not that. Butter is not okay. No wait, butter is okay. A glass of milk a day will make you stronger, or milk leaches calcium from your bones. I have also heard "You can eat whatever you want but all in moderation," and even that is not a good way to approach nutrition, either.

From my experience, what we put on the end of our fork matters. I've recently concluded that when it comes to personalized health, you need to be your own scientist. Gain the proper knowledge, put that knowledge into action, and the body will do the rest. People can talk about food, diet, and health all day long. It is different for everyone. What works for some does not always work for others.

From the moment of my diagnosis, I have been constantly acquiring information about cancer, ovarian cancer specifically. Dr. Fields suggested I investigate Dr. Nasha Winters. This by far is the best first step in finding accurate information. To build a bridge with cancer knowledge is difficult. *The Metabolic Approach to Cancer: Integrating Deep Nutrition, The Ketogenic Diet, and Nontoxic Bio-Individualized Therapies* by Dr. Nasha Winters, was eye-opening. It was the launching pad to want to learn more. So much so that I signed up for her live lectures. In one of these prerecorded video lectures I saw, she stated that no one is healthy. She asked, "Who here was healthy before they were first diagnosed?" Many in the audience raised their hands. She waited a moment, then proceeded to affirm that no one is truly healthy.

It all made sense. We live in a toxic world. How can we have any chance of being healthy? There is toxicity in our homes, bodies, and environments. It is sometimes too much for the human body. Our bodies have an incredible ability to heal themselves. In fact, when we do get sick, they intuitively know how to respond. They can kick out whatever toxins and diseases encroach on our bodies.

So, why are so many of us who think we are healthy "sick"? That is the magic question. A friend of mine, also a cancer survivor, explained it this way: for example, there is an abnormality in the body. The immune system gets off track, and that is when the disease attacks. Different people will have different ideas as to the answer. I for one am in a conundrum. I do not have an answer. This is where perspective comes into play. That is what influences the body. There was a lesson in all this.

Your beliefs become your thoughts,
Your thoughts become your words,
Your words become your actions,
Your actions become your habits,
Your habits become your values,
Your values become your destiny.
—*Mahatma Gandhi*

Yes, I may have made healthy choices, but somehow cancer still happened. No need to go down that road, as it leads to a never-ending cycle of shame and guilt. I had to analyze this on a much deeper level. The real "a-ha" moment was not to look back at what I *had been* doing, but to look ahead at what I could do today for a healthy future. To learn is to grow. To grow is how I can pass my storehouse of knowledge on to others. I had to figure this out. It is the foundation of how I can continue to stay disease free. My life will be full and long, as I will forever be open to learning what life has to offer and in turn pay it forward.

I highly recommend reading Dr. Nasha Winters' lifesaving book. To me, the knowledge was priceless. Her experience, providing information on how I can live a better, healthier life, helped me understand the disease on a deeper level. I cannot change the world out there, only the choices I make in my world. I understand the importance of making better choices: physically, mentally, and spiritually.

My nutrition choices throughout my life have been sketchy. My health history is important, as it can shine a light as to where I am today. When I was younger, my parents made sure we ate healthily. There was never a shortage of nutritious food—homemade meals. We went out to eat maybe once a year. Fast food was not our thing, so on a road trip it was a treat. My dad would always say, "Keep your eyes on your fries." My hometown did not even have a fast-food joint until the '90s. I do have to admit I always had a sweet tooth. Even with my parents' best efforts I still had a candy stash. Whenever I got my allowance, it went straight to candy. I even had a candy tooth that the dentist had to pull out because it turned black and green. I know it's pretty gross!

When I was ten and we moved, as I have told you, from a small town in Canada to Dallas, Texas, it was a big change. There was one place I remember more than any other: it delivered pizza right to your door. Not only was I impressed with an actual pizza hut, but it also delivered. We always cooked homemade pizzas—delicious by the way, but this was new. Pizza delivery. Oh, man, I am in heaven. I loved to go out to eat. I still do. Even though I had what I think was a small candy addiction and a love for junk food, I still stayed pretty fit. I was very active, so I guess it all balanced out. As the years passed, I had little concern about what I was eating, especially in college, and into my twenties.

I started getting chronic migraines when I was twenty-six. These migraines forced me to make better food choices. I feel it was God's way of stopping me in my tracks. Guiding me to be more conscious. For as long as I can remember, I have always loved food! Who doesn't? My life choices built up over time are why I had chronic migraines.

I spent several years bouncing from doctor to doctor, trying to figure out why I had them, often lasting for a week, sometimes two weeks. Not one doctor, even specialists, could find an answer. No one could figure out why. I now know that there was a reason, there was not an answer. The doctors I saw were treating the aftermath. Treating the migraines after I had them. What I really needed was to go further as to why I was getting them. There would be short periods of momentary relief. The treatments worked for a short time, but they would always come back.

Then I found a doctor like no other I had ever met. Dr. Jackie Fields. She was one of the few doctors with any idea why I was getting migraines. I remember the first time I met her she treated me like a person, not a case. She has a passion to help, sharing her experience and expertise so people can live as healthily lives as possible. She treated all of me, and not just the aftermath of the migraines. It was a miracle that I found her, and that I was able to get myself and my kids as patients.

Dr. Fields is an integrative, homeopathic doctor. She knew there was a "why" I was having migraines and did not stop until we found an answer. Her vast knowledge of, well, everything still amazes me. I have learned so much life-altering information from her.

With her knowledge and the help of my engineer husband, we figured out that amongst other things I was allergic to soy. My migraines stemmed from a leaky gut and unbalanced hormones. I spent two years on a rigorous diet that helped me with my leaky gut. Soon after that, I got pregnant with my daughter. My leaky gut issues had been addressed, and my hormones balanced out. Needless to say, things turned around. I no longer have migraines.

Dr. Fields has been my life coach—a North Star—teaching me what it truly means to be healthy. We live in a very toxic world, and this does not have to be the case. Having her in my corner is one of the many reasons we love her, and why she feels like a part of the family.

Not only am I focusing on what is at the end of my fork. I also am often neurotic with what I put on my body. Ever since my migraines, I cannot abide man-made chemical smells. If it is natural —for instance, from a plant—I am fine, but anything else and I start feeling sick. My body tells me by having headaches and feeling nauseous. My sensitivity to chemical smells is borderline insane. Once, flying home from my grandmother's in Canada, we were waiting to board. Roger ran out of deodorant and borrowed some. It was Axe. I wanted so badly to be okay with it. Finally, I had to ask Roger if he could go into the airport bathroom and wash his armpits. I am sure you have been in an airport bathroom—often not the most private place. He did this, as he knew I would otherwise be a hot mess all the way home. My body was giving me signs in the form of headaches to tell me to stay away from harsh toxic chemicals.

As time went on, I made it my job to buy only what had natural ingredients. Especially when we brought kids into the world. This goes for soaps, body and hand lotions, shampoos, sunscreen . . . anything that goes on or in my body. I make sure it's as natural and toxic free as can be. It adds a few dollars to our budget but is worth it. Toxins in our bodies can do more harm than I can even wrap my head around.

Being healthy doesn't fall into what we put in, on and around our bodies. Those are just some pieces in the puzzle. The other pieces I focus on are being physically, mentally, and spiritually healthy. The nutritional piece is the ringleader—a way for the other health factors to follow. What we eat matters. What we think matters. What we feel matters, and what we do matters! It all goes together, but if I do not start with a healthy diet, the other pieces will not fit. My health will not be strong. It all aligns to make my world balanced.

I have been living like this for over a decade. It is why I had to really question how I had gotten cancer. The main reason I had been headstrong about nutrition and toxins was to avoid diseases like cancer. It was quite baffling. For a slight moment, I asked myself: "*Why in the world should I continue this lifestyle? Why keep making the same decisions I had been making all these years? It did not matter. I ended up with cancer, anyway.*

I did not let this thinking go on for any length of time. For a bit, that's just how I felt, but did not entertain these thoughts, by any means. I continue to enhance my health. If I want to increase my chances of staying on this earth longer, I need to make healthy choices.

I have a routine I follow almost every day. It is a strategy, a way of life for people who want to live the life of their dreams. This all came from a webinar led by Hal Elrod, author of *Miracle Mornings*. The takeaway I got from this webinar is to start every morning with S.A.V.E.R.S.

S: Silence — Meditate

Meditating is simpler than I was making it out to be. Meditation to me was to sit cross-legged with my eyes closed and try not to think. To find the light and the total stillness, calm, peace, and balance. I tried to sit in silence without thinking. It is quite difficult.

As I came to find out, that is not exactly what meditation is. It is the time to sit with my thoughts and mind. I heard a podcast just recently that the monkey mind is a part of meditation. I learned that meditating means to take the time to sit with my thoughts and not worry about whatever comes into my mind. This practice is to help with the rest of my day. Meditation helps my brain organize my thoughts so there is little confrontation, or time wasted with stress, throughout the day. I have been doing this for a little while now. When I do not get to it, I can really see a difference in how my day plays out.

A: Affirmations — Daily on words that support my goals

Some of my go-to phrases are, "I trust," "I am calm," "I'm at ease," "I am healthy," "I am happy at this moment," "I am at peace."

I recite many affirmations each day. They plant a seed as to who I want to BE, What I want to DO, and What I will HAVE because of it.

V: Visualize — seeing my future as being cancer free.

I have mainly two prominent visualizations:

- One for Cancer: to have a disease-free body. I visualize sunlight beaming through my body with healing powers.
- One for my future: depicted in an enormous yard with flowers and a landscape just like in *The Secret Garden*—sun shining down through the canopy of the giant trees, my family playing games, children running around. Basically, like a giant Easter gathering with my whole family—grandchildren and all. No matter how the scene changes, the family is always there.

E: Exercise — I exercise every day, even if it is just a walk.

My main practices: yoga, Manic Training, walking, swimming. If I keep moving, I know that will keep me healthy long enough to ski down the slopes with my grandchildren.

R: Read — Reading books to help me reach my goals in life.

As I told you, I was not a fan of reading until my late twenties. And now I am writing a book. No words to describe how much this means to me. So incredible. The books I read this past year have been true lifelines. I read at least ten to twenty minutes a day. Whether audio or text format, it does not matter, just as long as it is a book that enhances my knowledge to support a happy and healthy life. A list of recommended titles is at the end of *Knowing the B.A.S.I.I.C.S.*

S: Scribe — Journaling/ Writing

Journaling has never been my forte. I have been keeping a journal for about a year now. It is another lifeline I fold into my daily routine because, for one, it holds me accountable, and it guides me to my true purpose in life. My writing has a constant theme: family, growth, and gratitude. I feel I am a product of the ripple effect, and it is my duty to keep it going. Implementing hope, peace and kindness in my life is priceless. I pinch myself to remind me that my life is real, not a dream! Journaling is a way to let everything go and just write. No matter the content, it helps me with my life's dreams one entry at a time.

There is a saying: *Form your habits, and your habits form you.* It is almost like I am craving the habits I have added into my life the last couple of months: daily meditation, yoga, writing, and reading. I feel so much more at ease. Things that used to bother me do not anymore. Cancer literally stopped me in my tracks. It put me on a unique path so that I could really start implementing these simple routines. These are little things that have enhanced every day. My heart is full, and I want to share it with the entire world!

---

1. World Health Organization, "WHO Remains Firmly Committed to the Principles Set Out in the Preamble to the Constitution,"
https://www.who.int/about/governance/constitution."
2. "Determinants of Health," World Health Organization, February 2017, https://www.who.int/news-room/q-a-detail/determinants-of-health.

Chapter 11

Let Go of "I know"—Learn to Grow

> The Truth is not what you want it to be, it is what it is, and you must bend to its power or live a lie. —Miyamoto Musashi

Everything I have written in this book, I have learned from my personal experience, books, and inspirational stories. I continue to learn every day. Even then, the amount of knowledge out there is infinite. I will take in whatever the world throws at me and absorb it the best I can.

The days of writing, reading, and reflection have been transformational! Deep feelings surface that are overwhelming! So much so, in fact, that the only thing I know to do is channel those feelings into deep gratitude! It is such a gift to be guided to know what really matters in life. I continue to be awestruck, feeling truly blessed with these gifts—with that blessing I get to pass along to you.

Ovarian-cancer risk factors can go one of two ways, either reducing or increasing the risk. "It is what it is." No matter what the percentage was for me, I still, despite all the best efforts, got cancer. That does not mean your story will be the same. Knowing the risk factors helps. They give a guideline on how to minimize the chances. As far as I can tell and reading information from the Centers for Disease Control and Prevention, CDC, there are several ways to reduce the chances of getting ovarian cancer: being on birth control pills, having children, and breastfeeding. If you breastfeed or have had children, it decreases the number of times you ovulate, and the risk decreases as well. On the flip side, if you have kids after thirty, it increases the chances. I guess for me they canceled each other out. [1]

Taking birth control pills can reduce the risk. In my case, I could never take the pill. It would kind of send me into wonka doodle land. In other words, my moods were a bit all over the place. So I just never took them.

One significant piece of advice is, do not Google things to death. Being in tune with your body is the only evidence you need. Everyone is different. Even though I got cancer does not mean you have to or will. Do not ignore the B.A.S.I.I.C.S. Ignoring them will not make things go away. Ask the hard questions. The questions need to be answered so you can start a plan. Without the question, there is not a plan. Without a sound plan, there can only be a myriad of issues that will make life harder and open you up to unnecessary therapies. The earlier you detect anything, the better! This does not mean that there is a guarantee that things will be all rainbows and unicorns. Early detection is just so important!

Reducing toxicity in our environment is crucial. With each passing day, conservation awareness goes up. Efforts are being made, and it is becoming a common practice to treat our planet with care. The more people are aware of how horribly we are treating our planet and bodies, the more we can work towards this collaborative goal. A common goal to preserve our planet and bodies and reduce the toxicity. Not only will it reduce disease, but also it will ensure that this earth is around for billions of years to come, until the sun burns out. An attainable task, one person at a time. Think of it as the ripple effect! One person can make all the difference in the world, and that person can be you! Have you ever heard the quote about a mosquito from the Dalai Lama? "If you think you are too small to make a difference, try sleeping with a mosquito." With enough people working together, there can be a mass movement to create a healthy earth for generations to come. I believe that with all my heart!

The controversy of what is toxic and what is not is complex. It seems like we can't eat, do, touch, smell anything without there being a link to a disease. It can be so overwhelming that instead of tackling problems in small doses, sometimes we do nothing at all. Sometimes I wish I did not know what I know because I can't unlearn it.

This of course makes it fun for my kids. Their parents know too much about health. Yes, we are total buzz kill, but that does not matter (one of the best pieces of advice I got from Dr. Fields). As parents, we are their first pallet. That means we are the ones who give our kids their first taste of food.

I hope we give them the knowledge and live by example. Hopefully, they will make healthy decisions now and when they get older. Planting the seed and nurturing it is all we can do. Ultimately, they will choose. That does not stop me from trying. It is my job as a parent to help guide their choices. Be there to support whatever path they take, and then hopefully they will not have too many mistakes to learn from.

---

1. "What Can I Do to Reduce My Risk of Ovarian Cancer?" March 15, 2021, Division of Cancer Prevention and Control, Centers for Disease Control and Prevention, https://www.cdc.gov/cancer/ovarian/basic_info/prevention.htm.

Chapter 12

A Healing Success Story!

> Your positive action combined with positive thinking results in positive success. — Shiv Khera

In a nutshell, this whole experience has been a success. Ideal, not so much! I mean, it is cancer. The timing and how this all unfolded definitely played a part! When I mentioned writing a book my doctors were all for it! Dr. Fields supported me, as she too knows the importance of a good healing story. She told me that telling my story is a way for me to *live it and let it go*. Dr. Guntupalli agreed wholeheartedly that my story was indeed a success!

The word *success*—that can mean lots of things. Success for me changes you. If you know how I roll by now, I find success in most anything I do. In this present scenario, the fact that I feel good and as of today I do not have any cancer is truly a success! I am in remission, which is so incredibly amazing! Getting to have more time with my family means everything to me. I beat this thing. I can have a normal life without the constant fight! The growth I have experienced is immeasurable! I am grateful that I was willing enough to accept "what is" and all that came with it.

From the moment I found out I had stage 3C ovarian cancer, it has made things in my life a lot more intense!

On Monday, September 18, 2019, came the official diagnosis. By December 2019, I was in remission. That fast. In the blink of an eye. Looking back, it seems longer. Even now, it seems like it happened years ago. Funny how time works. When we were in it, it seemed like it was forever. This is because we were in a literal survival mode for months. Having the diagnosis of cancer seems like a dream—almost like it was someone else's story.

Several months after my last infusion, I was living in a quasi-dreamworld. This dreamworld helped me for a while. My life went on as I slowly got my strength back. Even though I had literally just been through the most challenging time of my life, I somehow was able to pretend that chapter was closed.

Well, that is the funny thing about cancer. It will always loom, no matter how long I am in remission. I need to remember that, as it will save my life again someday. If I forget and my body is giving me signs of recurrence, I may not be in the position to listen. If I am not able to listen, then I am just repeating history. Nobody wants that.

I have listened and learned in this journey. The universe is telling me to take care of myself, and that is just what I will continue to do. I shared today in my Colorado Ovarian Cancer Alliance (COCA) Yoga class that I had always thought I was taking care of myself, but this little experience suggests otherwise.

It reminds me of the children's story "We're Going on a Bear Hunt" by Michael Rosen. Such a wonderful story with so much meaning—about a family who goes on a bear hunt. Grabbing their flashlights, they start out the door. With each step of their journey, they come across difficult terrain. These different terrains include muck, water, weeds, and wind. A constant refrain throughout the book is, "Can't go under it. Can't go over it. Gotta go through it."

They are going through it together. Going through challenges with someone is where strength is found.

I love it when it rains: the smell, the sound. It is therapeutic. Just take a moment and imagine sitting in a nice, cozy home with a blanket wrapped around you. A little window open just slightly. Slowly, you hear the first drops of rain fall. With the windows open, you can breathe in the aroma. Nothing distracts you, as you are curled up in the warm blanket, watching the rain, witnessing it fall from the sky to the ground. So peaceful!

Now, let your mind expand to where the raindrops came from. From the sky, of course, but it's so much more than that. The rain, like us, connects to the synergy of the universe. I feel I am just like a raindrop—being a part of something magical that is so much bigger than me. In the big picture, a raindrop is part of the big, beautiful ocean, and the ocean is a part of the raindrop. That is how I feel. I am a part of something unbelievably magnificent.

My newfound routine of yoga, meditation, journaling, and reading is taking me deeper into that ocean. I am not unique, or different from anyone else. I just had this time of incredible opportunity to find purpose. To me, that is a success all in its own. I was able to embrace the diagnosis. Instead of wondering why I got cancer, I immediately tried to find ways to survive it. Honestly, I am still learning. It helped me become more aware and focus on what really matters in life!

Getting cancer happened. It was a scary time. I no longer need to be fearful. I got rid of the fear and turned it into faith. The blessing lies in having a deeper understanding and seeing the beauty in all of this—the layers of armor I've removed. Life is so much better when not having to complain, compare, or criticize. To be successful has so much more meaning if I am understanding, true, honest, and grateful.

I strive to be a spiritual being living in a human world. The differences in people are fascinating. Humans all over the world are searching for their purpose, their "why?" If I pay attention long enough, I get to learn from their experience. I think it is my moral duty to give back what has been so freely given to me! Having gone through my cancer journey, I can help others—be there, share my experience. Give hope, especially in the darker times.

Some days are better than others. Being present in the moment —that's when miracles happen, and the healing stories begin!

I need to act today to make sure that I am here on this earth for my family. I'm supposed to be here! I am going to be here. I tell my husband all the time that even though cancer has graced our doorstep, it does not mean it is coming back. While working on this book, I heard him on a call for work. I didn't mean to eavesdrop, but I speculated from the conversation that they were planning trips for the future. He said he wants to be here in case I get sick again. I waited a moment . . . then yelled, "Not going to happen!"

Here you are, you made it through the book. There is not a lovable furry old monster at the end. Instead, there is a more insightful beautiful you. You turned each page, pages that could very well have come from you.

I know that cancer exists in many forms, and therefore, it's so important to pay attention to our mind, bodies, and surroundings. No matter what happens in the future, I am grateful. For it all. This is a journey that I did not want to take, but I embraced it. I have walked in the footsteps of thousands of women. That does not make me special. It just means that I am one more person who can help pave the path for you! We have not crossed the finish line yet...keep reading there are some goodies at the end of the book! No monsters! I promise!

15 Informative Life-Saving Tips to Increase Longevity

Choose one and start to change your life today!

1. Get plenty of restorative rest.

2. Surround yourself with positive like-minded people.

3. Buy clean products for your home and body.

4. Keep screen-containing electronics out of the room when we sleep. Dr. Fields shared this with me.

5. Use glass and stainless-steel containers when possible.

6. Get involved in a support group-no matter what is going on in your life.

7. Buy organic if possible.

8. Buy food from the farmer's market or a local farm (in person or online).

9. Focus on healthy foods—whole foods—and mainly stay away from processed grain, industrial oils, and white sugar. (Do we still eat these? Yes, but they are not staples in our home.)

10. Confront feelings—don't suppresses them—as described below:

SSS—Spot, Stop, Swap [1]

- SPOT— Spot and recognize the feeling.
- STOP—Understand what the feeling is and label it. Saying it out loud and expressing who we feel.
- SWAP—Find a positive perspective to proceed to the next moment.

11. Practice
conservation and other habits to help the environment (use cloth napkins instead of paper—the amount of water saved, not to mention wood, is mind-boggling).
12. Think optimistically—thoughts can be as toxic as material products in our environment.
13. Be kind to yourself and others—do a random act of kindness.
14. Give yourself permission to find your authentic self.
15. Exercise every day.

The more awareness we have about what we eat, how we feel, what we think, and what
we do—the longer we can live without "dis-ease" in our world.

—Trish Kifer

Jay Shetty, Think Like a Monk: Train Your Mind for Peace and Purpose, New York: Simon & Schuster (2020), 33.

Takeaways

If you have any signs or symptoms, go get checked. No matter what you think it is, it does not hurt to get things checked out. If not now, when? Be your own advocate in addition to finding a health or patient advocate to assist you throughout your journey, especially in the beginning. I did not need one, as my team was on it every step of the way.

Take time for *you*. Take the sun and the moon, for example. Our bodies are comprised of solar and lunar parts. When the sun is up, it's a time for moving activity. When the moon is out, it should be a time for resting and restoring. The yang/yin harmony between the two is essential. Taking time for yourself will help with your awareness, help you be in harmony with how the universe presents itself to you. I am surely not saying to follow in my footsteps, as it took me having cancer. Take the time now to stop and take in what's important. The universe sent me signs before I even knew they were there. The signs were always there for me to notice. I just was not listening closely enough. Now I am!

Do anything you can think of to get or stay healthy. Keep moving and get plenty of restorative rest. I know when I do not exercise or get a good night's sleep, I feel all out of sorts. It does not need to be over the top. I found exercise routines I enjoy. Whether

I go for a walk, practice yoga, or step it up and go to Manic, it all helps me keep my health status up. Mostly, it just harmonizes my day.

Live in the present moment. This is huge! I have only been practicing this a few months. Making the time for stillness gives space for the rest of the day to unfold in remarkable ways. I realized right away that as I sat and meditated, I was finding more peace within myself. My thinking is clearer, and I can see a direct path to a feeling of calmness. Being present in the moment, to be *in the now*, has helped me immensely. This has been a game changer, more so once I went into remission. It helps me with wandering thoughts. The more I am mindful, the more I am in the moment, the more I will be healthy. Every moment, one moment at a time, with clarity and understanding.

No matter how daunting the cancer stats are, remember that there are thousands of cancer survivors out there. A message passed on to me from my mom's friend Muffy, who had colon cancer and was given three months to live. That was fifty years ago. Stay in the happy stories your mind and heart are listening!

> Do things that make everything easier and other things unnecessary. — Geoff Woods, and Jay Papasan, *The ONE Thing*

I am here for you! Taking that first step into the cancer world is scary. Just like in *Monster at the End of This Book.* It is only lovable and, furry old Grover. That is, if you focus things in that direction. It does not need to be so scary. Taking one step, one day, one moment, at a time will be forever helpful! It makes a world of difference to have a positive perspective on things and to know what you can and can't control.

I have been there, blessed to have an amazing support team. I am going to assume it will be the same for you. I will be a part of your team and you are mine. It would be an honor.

Below, I quote from a poem that is under the bell I got to ring after my last chemo treatment:

Fate whispers to the warrior . . . "You cannot withstand the storm," and the warrior whispers back, "I am the storm!"
We now call my team
"Trish's Storm"

This is a moving, living story. As I am moving and living! No matter how much I do right in keeping this disease at bay, I will never have control of if or when it decides to reoccur. With cancer that is just the nature of the disease, and I am okay with that. I am not cancer and cancer is not me. In some way cancer will always be a part of my life. I just get to choose how much! No matter what, I am a cancer survivor by the way I live my life, cancer or no cancer.

Acknowledgments

I am truly honored, and grateful to share my story with you. Somehow, the energy I felt from the universe came from the need to hear healing stories. In some way, this book materialized because of energy from you. Even if you do not realize it, it is there. This is a story that needed to be told, and I thank you for your inspiration to write it.

Everyone in the book, I hold dear in my heart. Writing the acknowledgments was quite difficult. In countless ways, my support group is the reason I am alive today. In no way do I say this lightly. I believe with everything in me that my tribe, with their limitless love, and the universe's timing is why I am in remission. I am just going to say it. They are why I am a survivor! I can declare this with all certainty because they were with me, holding my hand, physically and mentally, praying, collaborating, celebrating, encouraging, and supporting me every single day! They gave me strength, and inspiration that I could not muster on my own. I am so humbled and grateful to have you in my life.

One person in particular whom I want to thank is Ben. I mentioned him earlier in the book. He was only eleven years old. Sadly, he lost his fight with cancer during the writing of this book. If I was having a hard day, I would think of Ben and tell myself: *If he can do it, so can I.* As his therapies were exeptionally hard. There's an unwritten bond that no one wants to have. I was blessed to have it with Ben. On some level we knew what each other was going through. I am a better person because of him. On behalf of Ben, I want to help spread his love and kindness. His spirit is strong. By our doing kind things, he can live on through us—making the world a better place one kind act at a time.

Be Kind. #OnBehalfOfBen

Thank you to my dear fellow members of Colorado Ovarian Cancer Alliance (COCA)

A special thank-you to my dear friend Tish for your loving energy and healing hands!

Thank you to my tribe at Manic. I cherish your kindness, support, and inspiration!

Thank you to my Good Vibe troop—Melissa W., Serena P., and Kiana B., and Amy D.—for always knowing what I needed even before I did, for all the thoughtful gifts, and for being there for me and my family. You are amazing, and I am so blessed to have you in my life!

Thank you to my sister friends—as Kela would put it—Emily, April, Beth, and Kelli. Thank you for being the best friends a person could ask for. You help keep me sane, and I truly value our friendship. Love you, beautiful ladies!

A tremendous thank-you to the amazing Usual Suspects—Cole, Angie, George, Tim, Renee, Christie and Melanie. I will always be grateful for your generosity, and kindness. At every turn, you gave me such amazing gifts, that in turn were actually little treasures of hope!

Thank you, Dr. Guntupalli. From the moment we met, I knew we were going to be the right fit. The communication with you and your team was impressive. You answered every question and concern with understanding and compassion. We threw everything at this cancer, even the kitchen sink, and it is another reason why I am here today to talk about it. Thank you for helping me be able to live my life to its fullest!

Thank you, Dr. Fields. I appreciate you not only as my doctor, but as a person. There was no doubt an inevitable war going on in my body. Considering how hard I was being hit, you knew how to limit the blows with your integrative expertise. The collaboration you had with Dr. Guntupalli was life changing, as I needed you both to come up with the best strategy to win this battle! I also want to thank you, for your encouraged me to write my story. Now here we are, with yet another healing story to help others on their journey. Thank you for your kindness and for always having my back!

A heartfelt thank-you to my incredible family!

Thank you, Roger. You will stop at nothing to protect our family. This diagnosis was not something you could protect me from, so you did the next best thing. You never left my side. At every turn, every appointment, every infusion, every surgery, every test result, you were there. You have always been supportive in whatever direction my passion leads me. Thank you for supporting me and helping me make this all happen. On some level, I know you wanted me to share my story too. Not only because it is the right thing to do, but to help the husbands out there going through this with their wives. Thank you for being my rock!

Thank you to my spirited, empathetic, thoughtful, loving kids. Kela and Ryan. I want to thank you for your resiliency, and ability to change course with understanding at every turn. I appreciate the special times we got to share when my energy was down. I hope you will remember the time not as when Mom had cancer, but as the time we got to read the Harry Potter series and play family fun ball, even though I would sometimes only have the energy to just stand there. Or lie in bed, reading and snuggling. I cherish our morning walks together and our discussions of with all kinds of topics. I am proud to be your mom! You two are the best kids any mom could ever ask for!

Mom and Dad, thank you for your compassion and inspiration. For the times where I could just call, and know when I got off the phone, I would feel better. Thank you for your help with the family. Coming up to take care of the kids so Roger could be by my side. I am grateful for our loving relationship and your incredible generosity and kindness! I am so thankful for your support and for always believing in me!

Thank you, Mitch, for always encouraging me to be my best me! You are my big brother, and I am proud of your strength, both physically and mentally You have always paved the way for excellence and gave me great big footsteps for me to follow! You married one of my favorite people, Ira, my beautiful sister-in-law. I appreciate your kindness, encouragement, and love! Thank you for being the best big brother and sister anyone could ask for!

There are no words to express how grateful I am for my clan, whom, I love more than anything in the world! You are my everything!

TURKS&CAICOS
ISLAND

My Personal Life-changing Book Recommendations

- Coelho, Paulo. *The Alchemist: A Fable about Following Your Dream.*
- Elrod, Hal. *The Miracle Morning: The Not-So-Obvious Secret Guaranteed to Transform Your Life Before 8 AM.*
- Guntupalli, Saketh R., MD, and Maryann Karinch. *Sex and Cancer: Intimacy, Romance, and Love after Diagnosis and Treatment.*
- Keller, Gary, and Jay Papasan. *The ONE Thing: The Surprisingly Simple Truth behind Extraordinary Results.*
- Kwik, Jim. *Limitless: Upgrade Your Brain, Learn Anything Faster, and Unlock Your Exceptional Life.*
- Matthews, John. *Healing the Wounded King: Soul Work and the Quest for the Grail.*
- Muth, Jon J. *The Three Questions* (based on a story by Leo Tolstoy)
- Rosen, Michael. *We're going on a Bear Hunt*
- Shetty, Jay. *Think Like a Monk: Train Your Mind for Peace and Purpose Every Day.*

• Stone, Jon. *There is a Monster at the End of this Book* (starring lovable, furry old Grover).

• Tolle, Eckhart. *The Power of Now:* A Guide to Spiritual Enlightenment.

• Winters, Dr. Nasha, ND, FABNO, and Jess Higgins Kelley, MNT. *The Metabolic Approach to Cancer: Integrating Deep Nutrition, the Ketogenic Diet, and Nontoxic, Bio-Individualized Therapies.*

Articles I Recommend

• Roth, Andrew J. "5 Myths about Ovarian Cancer." Memorial Sloan Kettering Cancer Center. September 16, 2019. In which Dr. Dennis Chi, Deputy Chief of the Gynecology Service and Head of Ovarian Cancer Surgery at Memorial Sloan Kettering, debunks some myths about cancer. https://www.mskcc.org/news/5-myths-about-ovarian.

• Yamada, Diane, MD, and Kathryn Mills, MD. "What Every Woman Should Be Aware of about Ovarian Cancer." September 17, 2020. Northwest Community Healthcare. https://www.nch.org/news/what-every-woman-should-be-aware-of-about-ovarian-cancer/.

Additional Resources

Sloan Kettering Institute: With over seventy years of cancer research, Sloan Kettering Institute scientists have been widely recognized by national and international organizations for their innovative work in science and medicine. https://www.mskcc.org/cancer-care/types/ovarian

SHARE Cancer Support: A nonprofit organization, SHARE is dedicated and experienced; it helps support and empower women affected by breast, ovarian, uterine, or metastatic breast cancer.
https://www.sharecancersupport.org

About the author

Trish Kifer was born in Canada, where she spent the first ten years of her life. Her family moved to North Texas, where she spent her formative years. After graduating from Texas Tech University, she taught in elementary education for the next decade. At the age of twenty-seven, she moved to Fort Collins, Colorado, where she met her future husband, Roger, and they are now raising their two children, Lokela and Ryan. An athlete that thrives in challenges mentally and physically, she also enjoys traveling with her family to engage, learn, and grow in life experiences from other cultures. She is a proud cancer survivor, intent on helping raise ovarian-cancer awareness and encouraging others to share their healing stories.

Thank you

Dear Beautiful, Wonderful You,

Thank you for reading my book! Below, is my contact information. If you would not mind, let me know how you found out about this book.

As you know by now, I love to hear stories about how the universe works. Write to tell me how this book found you. This is only if you want to. I just am so grateful that these words found their way to you.

I was just telling my husband that these words I wrote were not from me. I mean yes, technically they are, but as I go back and read what I have written, I don't really remember writing them.

Something bigger than me has helped get these words out to you. This incredible opportunity that I took to write to you means the world to me! To help someone find the way to a doctor to find the cancer before its progression is a genuine gift! I made a deal with myself and my higher power to live on and help others in the name of those I have loved and lost. They will always live in my heart. My passion to bring this story to light was inspired entirely by nothing more than to save lives. I hope it has found you in time!

Warmly yours,

Trish

trishkifer@hope-journeys.com

www.hope-journeys.com

Please leave a review

You can help spread ovarian-cancer awareness.
The more books read, the more lives saved.
Please leave me an honest review on Amazon sharing one takeaway that you got from this book.
My genuine gratitude and sincere appreciation!

All my best—Trish

Made in the USA
Middletown, DE
26 April 2022

64804407R00086